© Text – Margaret Flaws

© Illustrations – Bridget Woodford

Published by

Designed and printed at
The Orcadian Limited
Hatston
Kirkwall
Orkney
KW15 1DW
www.orcadian.co.uk

ISBN 0 9540320 8

Thord's Story

By Margaret Tait Flaws

Illustrated by Bridget Woodford

ACKNOWLEDGEMENTS

I am in debt to many people for help in researching this book. The following are some of the names:

The staff of The Orkney Library & Archive
Tom Muir and Anne Brundle from The Orkney Museum
Katrina Mainland
Brian Smith, The Shetland Archives
W. P .L. Thomson
Colin Rendall
Johnny Johnston
Rae Phillips from Boardhouse Mill
Eileen Norquoy
John Crossley

From Norway:
Anne Tone Aanby
Bjørn Aksdal
Rolf Heggnes
Liv Schei

For calendars, moons and tides, my husband Ian, sons Magnus and Dod, and nephew John Sinclair.

Introduction

The sixteenth century in Orkney is not well documented. Historical events have been recorded but a picture of domestic life is hard to find. Whenever I mentioned to anyone that I was trying to find material for the year 1557 I was told: "Try 1750!" 1557 however is a notable year in Orkney history. Orcadians, as a rule, when asked the question, "When was the last battle on Orkney soil?", will generally answer, "The battle of Summerdale." This is not so. The hero of Summerdale, Edward Sinclair, fought another battle, over three days, against the English in Kirkwall in 1557 at Papdale. The Orcadians won. It seemed important to give some prominence to this battle also so I began my hunt for details of ordinary life at that time.

The first step was to choose names. Many names are recorded in Orkney from this period. It was a period of change, from Norse patronymics to settled surnames in the Scottish style. Norse names were changed to Scots, for example Kolbein became William. It is usually thought that the name George was substituted for Sigurd, but I thought it possible that the name Thord might have become George. My main reason for this is that Dod is the short form of George and in Iceland Dod is the short form of Thord. The other names are mostly from Norse as I felt that in Birsay there would still have been a number of traditional names.

At this period also the Norn would still have been the language spoken by most of the people outside of Kirkwall. My authority for this comes from two sources. The principal one is Jo Ben's Description of the Isles of Orkney, written in the sixteenth century. He states that the people do not say "Guid day, guid man." Instead they say "Goand da, boundae." There are also mentions in court records of people being unable to speak Scots although a hundred years had passed since Scotland had taken over the administration of Orkney.

To make the account as accurate as possible I wanted to use the correct days to correspond with the dates. I feel sure that people then would have been aware of the date as there were many Saints' days and, at the least, the priest would have reminded them. The dates used are accurate but they are, of course, those of the Julian calendar, which was in use then. This explains the fact that Johnsmas, which should be Midsummer Day, is ten days earlier. The Internet is a good source of information of this kind and I also found the phases of the moon for 1557. This means that the tides for the journey from Birsay are accurate also, thanks to my husband and son, both skippers.

There followed the problem of how they lived. There is no record of the house and steading at Kirkbuster being under one roof. However I felt that it was possible that in 1557 there was just one long building there as most of the farms at that time were built in that way. Winters at that time were colder than the present day and the benefit of having everything under one roof would be clear. Added warmth would come from the animals at either side of the living rooms.

There are few sources of information on farming practices at that time but it is possible to visualise what they must have been, from earlier and later records. Bere was the staple crop and there was enough grown for Orkney to export good quantities to Shetland and Norway. Oats were grown too and oat straw was needed, as the straw from bere was too soft to use for ropes or baskets. It is sometimes said in Orkney that the men imprisoned here during the Napoleonic

War taught the Orcadians how to weave straw to make the traditional Orkney chairs. Whatever the truth of that, straw was being used for ropes and caisies long before that so there was no lack of skill in weaving straw. It would have been a winter's task, round the fire in the evening.

Discovering which crops were grown proved to be a little difficult. Bere is, of course, a very old crop and has been known since Saxon times in Britain. It was known then as bære, the word we still use in Orkney. As the crop changed further south, so did the name, to become barley. Oats however proved more difficult. The heavy black oats grown in Orkney until recently were not introduced here until the seventeenth century. With a great deal of help from many people, it was finally settled that a different type of black oats would have been grown. The methods of tilling the land and sowing the crop can be found in an appendix to Jo Ben's book. Although the date of this is not known, it is the nearest in time to the period dealt with in this book. In this account also we discover that it was the task of the men to handle the crops. Women did not thresh or winnow the corn.

At that time there was a mill at Kirkbuster. The Barony Mill has a long history and would certainly have been there at that time though probably not in exactly the same place. There is, however, a clear record of a mill at Kirkbuster then and indeed there would have been many small mills within easy reach of the farms.

Research on vegetables produced a list from James Wallace's book, which would have been rather more than a hundred years later. By the time he was writing, cabbage had been introduced to Orkney, commonly thought to be by Cromwell's men. However kale had been grown in Scotland since at least the fifteenth century. It had been grown in Europe for a very long time. It seemed logical to assume that kale was grown here too. Peas and beans also were grown as the stalks and leaves helped to fertilize the ground.

There is no record of bees being kept in Orkney at that time, but there is evidence from Scottish sources that bees were an important part of farming in the days before the Reformation. The wax was needed for candles for the churches and was part of the tithes. The honey itself had many uses, not least preserving butter for the winter. This is documented from Shetland at this time and therefore presumably we can expect it to be used in the same way in Orkney. I did not feel that it would have been possible to collect enough honey and wax from wild bees to supply all this, so I decided that Kirkbuster, as it was a large holding, would have kept bees. Hives at this time were made of straw, presenting no problem to an Orkney farmer

It was, however, more difficult to decide how the sheep were managed. The breed of sheep was not the question. They would have been the same small breed as the North Ronaldsay ones or keeros now are. The bigger, heavier sheep had yet to be introduced. The problem lay in the management of them. They were kept on the common land and were rounded up on 'Beulding Day' so that people could sort out which sheep and lambs belonged to them. They were identified by a system of ear marks, a system used in North Ronaldsay still. The bailiff and the lawrightmen had to be there to see fair play.

They had also to be rooed, their fleeces taken from them, at some point in the year, and this proved a difficulty. The two accounts of this nearest in time to 1557 state that they were rooed in May or early June. It has been argued that this is much too early and that it might have been as late as July. I decided that I had to keep as closely as I could to the two relevant sources, combined Beulding Day and the rooing into one and put it in late May.

The method of rounding up the sheep is probably fairly accurate, as most sources suggest that the dogs were not used for rounding up but for catching individual sheep who had strayed. They were also used for catching individual sheep for rooing. I have used the children for this as the book revolves around them, but in fact they would have been caught by the dogs.

The incident with the eagle is based on a statement in Wallace's book. He writes that eagles have been known to carry off young children and that, because of this and the fact that they take the young animals, anyone who kills an eagle is to have a hen from every house in the parish. It seemed to me that the method of getting the hens would involve the lawrightman.

Many of the Saints' days and fairs included in this book can be found in the works of Ernest Marwick in Orkney and Jessie Saxby in Shetland. I made the assumption that there would be no difference between the two places as they shared a common cultural history. If I found a custom in Shetland that would have been relevant at this period I believed that I would have found it in Orkney too. Thus when I came across a mention in Peter A. Jamieson's book on Shetland, 'The Viking Isles', of a two-stringed fiddle called a gue I was delighted. Here was an old instrument which could be used for dancing or entertainment. Thus began a complicated search for information, leading eventually to a Professor of Music in Voss in Norway. The gue could have been the forerunner of the Hardingfele. It is most likely that the tune was played on one string while the other acted as a drone.

I have also imported the Skeklers from Jessie Saxby, again because I thought it likely that we would have had a similar custom.

Information about the battle is thin in the extreme. There are a few facts. It was fought over three days and the final day's skirmish was at Papdale. Edward Sinclair was again the hero of the hour. The English did bring cannon ashore to fire at the castle and they had to leave these behind. The weather defeated them in the end when a sudden storm blew up and many of them were drowned trying to reach their ships. Their commander, Sir John Clare, was reported to have drowned too, but there is a later mention of him in a written record so he may have survived. The Orcadians did not lose a single man and they made a good profit out of it all. They had the cannon and they ransomed such prisoners as they had managed to capture.

The battle of Papdale is mentioned also in Jo Ben's account but he puts the date at 1502. He states that it was fought at the washing place and from Hossack we can find that the women of Kirkwall washed their clothes at Papdale, perhaps in the 'Ducky Pond'. The fact that Jo Ben has an account of the battle, albeit with the wrong date, suggests his account must have been written later than has been supposed.

St Olaf's Fair, the forerunner of the Lammas Market, would have seen traders and goods from many places. As most of the wood used for ploughs came from Os in Norway, as well as the 'flat-packs' for small boats, it would not be strange if there were other goods which came across. I felt it was safe to assume that there would have been some wooden horses from Dala in Sweden. These have a very long history. At that time they did not have the elaborate decoration that they have now, but they might have been painted in a bright colour.

Lastly, it was difficult to decide how big a part superstition played in the lives of people then. There is no doubt that it was a great influence on their lives but I find it hard to believe that they would have allowed it to rule everything they did. Orcadians have always had a healthy scepticism and I feel sure that this existed in 1557.

Thord's Story

Thord's Story

Tuesday, 2nd February, 1557 – Candlemas

Thord woke up suddenly. He had been dreaming but he could not quite remember what he had been dreaming about. Something to do with the Stoor Worm. He was sure that he had been fighting it all by himself but the dream was fading fast. He lay awake in his bed in the sallur wondering why he had wakened up so quickly. Usually he took a long time to waken and his father and mother would be shaking him and calling him 'sleepy-head'. Today though was different.

It was still dark but there was a faint glimmer of light coming through the open door and he could hear his mother raking out the peat fire on the back in the firehouse. He heard her call to the servant girl, Lina, to get up from her bed in the neuk in the firehouse.

He heard his grandfather say, "Morning, Ingirid," to his mother and tell her to let him know when the breakfast was ready. Grandfather slept in a bed in the firehouse where it was always warm. The fire on the back was kept alight at all times and it was banked up with peats very carefully each evening before they all went to bed. It would bring very bad luck to the house if the fire were ever to go out.

Grandfather's bed made a fine seat for Thord and his little sister Christane to sit on in the daytime. Grandfather had a big chair made of straw to sit in. It had wooden legs but the back and the seat were made of straw. Father had one too but grandfather's was extra cosy because it had a sheepskin over it. Thord curled up in it when grandfather was outside and he loved it. There were straw stools as well and mother usually sat on one of them. "I'm going to have a chair like Da's with a sheepskin in it when I grow up," thought Thord.

Christane was still asleep in the bed beside him. He heard his father grunting as he bent over to strap his rivlins onto his feet and then the light from the door was blocked for a second as his father went through to the firehouse.

"Is Dod wakened?" asked his mother.

"No, I think him and Christane are still sleeping," said his father.

"It's a wonder if he is," said his mother, "when you think what day it is."

And then Thord remembered. It was his birthday.

"I'm wakened, Mam," he shouted and heard his mother and father laugh.

He got up, pulled his tunic over his head and strapped on his own rivlins. The light from the liora was getting stronger when he went through to the firehouse but the smoke from the new peats on the back was swirling around the room.

"The wind's changed," said grandfather. "The skylan board would need to be shifted." Thord was still too small to reach the pole with the board on top so his father shifted it round and soon the smoke was disappearing up through the square hole.

"Well, Dod, boy," said his grandfather. "How does it feel to be nine? I'll give you a good wish today, from Old Dod to Peerie Dod." Thord had been named after his grandfather as was the custom and his grandfather had always been known by his nickname, Dod, as well.

His mother had finished scooping out the grains of bere, which had been drying in the big pot overnight, and Lina started to grind them with the quern-stones. She swung the pot over the fire again and asked Thord to get some water from the tub on the stone bench at the door. The sound of Lina grinding the bere finally wakened Christane and she wandered into the firehouse looking hopefully at the pot. Christane was always interested in her food.

Mother poured the meal into the pot and stirred until it thickened. Thord liked bursteen and helped to fetch the bowls and hand it round. He liked the morning and the evening best, he thought, when they were all sitting round the back together, his whole family. And Lina, too, of course, though sometimes he was not all that fond of Lina. She had a sharp tongue and used to tell him to get out of her way if she was working.

"Magnus," said his mother to his father, "there's not much meal left to make bannocks with. We'll need some more soon."

"I was going to dry some corn today," said father. "Dod can help me after we've fed the kye."

Up till today the weather had been bad. It had rained a lot and the wind had been blowing strongly for a long time; it seemed for weeks. Grandfather for some reason was quite pleased about this and when they complained about the weather he would say,

"If the lavro sings afore Candlemas,

"She'll greet twice as lang after."

"Da, Da!" said Christane. "I've never seen a lavro greeting. What way can it greet?"

Mother laughed. "He means that if we get good weather before Candlemas, we'll get twice as much bad weather after."

If it was raining or the wind was blowing very strongly, they would carry food for the kye from the barn, through the stable, through the sallur, through the firehouse and into the byre and never need to go outside at all.

Today, though, was a glorious day. The sun shone and there was little or no wind. It was even warm outside on the brig-stones and Thord followed his father out round the back to the outside door, past the door through to the byre, past the bus-herra, the large red stone lying at the sun side of the door for luck, and along the brig-stones to the yard.

He enjoyed tying the windleens of hay and carrying them from the skroo in the yard back in front of the house and into the byre. The six cows and their calves seemed pleased to see them, but the bull gave Thord a bored look as usual. He hated being tied up all winter.

His father then took a burning peat from the fire and carried it out to the barn. He lit the kiln and they began to spread grains of bere over the straw matting on the platform in the kiln so that the heat coming from the fire could dry them. "You must not let it get too hot or the corn will scorch," said his father. "We'll have to watch the fire carefully."

Thord looked round the barn. There were the flails for threshing the sheaves leaning against the wall. There were the straw baskets, some full of grain, which had been threshed and was now ready for drying and some empty ones ready to be filled. He had watched father and grandfather making them during the winter and he was pretty sure he could make one too. He had made a little one and mother had said it was splendid, just the thing for keeping the spoons in. She had hung his spoon-cubbie on the wall and it was very useful. Maybe he should make another one for her – but not tonight. Tonight was his birthday and he would get grandfather to tell his favourite story when they were all sitting round the fire.

"You know what we must do today, Dod?" said his father. "We have to get the pins off the plough, the ski pins and the markal pin, and steep them in ale."

"What do we do that for, Faither?" asked Thord.

"Well, we do it to make sure that the ploughing will be good and we will have good luck with the crops. But we do it too to make the pins harder and they need to be to go through the ground properly."

"Why do we have to do it today?"

"Because today is Candlemas and we always steep them on Candlemas Day."

Thord helped his father take the pins off the plough, which was kept in the barn too. They took them into the house and his father fetched a wooden tub to put them in. He poured some ale from the ale-kirn over them and set the tub near the fire to warm.

"Now we have to leave them there for a while and then we can take them out and dry them off up on the couples. They'll be fine and hard when we need them," said father.

"I'm hungry, Mam," said Thord. "Is there a while to wait for dinner?"

"A fair while," said his mother, "but you can have a bannock and cheese just now." She handed him a warm bannock just freshly cooked and a bit of the cheese which Lina had just fetched from the sallur where it was stored among the meal.

"I'm a bit hungry too," said his father hopefully.

"I'll have nothing left at this rate," said his mother. "Christane has already eaten some of it."

"She would," thought Thord. "She's always hungry. I'm sure she can smell Mam's baking from a mile away."

"Right," said father, "now we must set out for the kirk so we can get home before it gets dark. We must light our candle for Candlemas. Did you give the priest all the candles we made from the beeswax, Ingirid, or did you keep a few back for us?"

"I kept a few. We used some at Yule but there will be one to spare yet."

They wrapped some straw round their rivlins to walk over the muddy ground to the kirk. It was quite a distance away, almost two miles, so father carried Christane because she was still small. They left mother to look after the feast and grandfather to help her but father drove Lina to the kirk in front of him.

"It will be good for your soul, Lina," he said. Lina grumbled all the way there and moaned that it was cold and she needed to help with the dinner, but she stopped making a noise when they went into the kirk and she saw the priest there.

"Ah, Magnus, I thought you would come," said the priest, "and the bairns too. That's fine. Light your candle and we will say Mass."

Thord looked round the little kirk with its flickering points of light from the many candles. It had tiny windows high up in the walls which let in a little of the afternoon light but it was a thin, pale light compared to the gold sparkle all around him. He saw Father Harald smiling at him and he was glad he had come. Christane's eyes were wide open. Her mouth was too but for once she was not chattering. She had gone as silent as Lina.

The excitement grew as they walked back and Christane had found her voice again. Food was the thing she got really excited about. She kept asking father what they were going to get to eat. Father said "Wait and see."

And it was a wonderful feast. Mother had cooked some reestit mutton in the big pot with kale and knockit corn. But even better than the mutton and broth, there was a little smoked trout for everyone. This was a real treat and was Thord's favourite.

"It's the last of the trout from the drying shed," said his mother. "I saved it for your birthday."

They sat round the fire and ate as much as they could. Most of the light in the room now came from the fire but father had lighted the coly-lamp too. Thord thought back to the blaze of light in the kirk and then peered into the darkness of the firehouse.

"I still like this best," he thought. "It's warm and cosy and all my family are here. And Da is going to tell us a story."

"Right, Dod," said grandfather. "What story do you want tonight?" he asked although he knew what the answer would be.

"Can we have Assipattle and the Stoor Worm?" said Thord. Grandfather smiled. "I thought it would be that one," he said. So grandfather began the story, while mother and Lina carded wool and father was busy with his knife making teeth for the harrows.

"Once upon a time," said grandfather, "there was a family who lived on a farm on the hillside. There was mother and father and seven sons. The youngest son was called Assipattle. And why was he called that, do you think?"

"Because he was lazy and sat beside the fire all day and poked in the ashes," shouted Thord and Christane.

"That's right. He was really lazy and his brothers got fed up with him and with the tall stories he used to tell about all the brave things he had done when he had done nothing really. Well one day news came to them that the muckle Stoor Worm had been seen coming close to land. This was dreadful news for the muckle Stoor Worm was a huge monster, the biggest in the whole world. It was so big that it could stretch right round the world and woe betide anybody that came near him for he would gobble them up and they would never be seen again."

Thord listened to his grandfather telling the familiar story and was as entranced as if it had been the first time that he heard it. He did not know what bit of the story grandfather had reached when he fell asleep, but fall asleep he did and his father carried him through to bed.

Thord spent a happy night dreaming of battles with the Stoor Worm and of course he won. Of course he did. He was nine years old now and of course he would win.

Wednesday, 3rd February, 1557

Thord felt someone shaking him.

"Come on, sleepy-head, get up now," said his father. "It's broad daylight and we have to take the corn to the Mill."

"Can I get some breakfast first?" asked Thord.

"If you hurry," said father.

Thord scrambled into his clothes and tied up his rivlins any old way. He rushed through to the firehouse and found his grandfather and his father already eating their bursteen. Christane was eating hers too.

"Trust her!" thought Thord. "She's never far behind when there's food on the go."

Thord took his bowl of bursteen from his mother and looked sadly at it. He was hungry and he would eat it but it did not taste so good when there was only water to add to it and no milk. Da had ale on his bursteen, and his father did too, but Thord did not think he would like that any better than water.

"When will we have milk again, Mam?" he asked.

"It will be a few weeks till Osla calves," said mother. "I doubt we'll have to do without cheese for a while yet too. But we have plenty of butter left, so that's a mercy."

"We'll be off to the Mill as soon as we can," said his father. "What are you thinking to do today?"

"Lina and I will put out some loads of dung," said Mother. "It's high time we put some out or the kye will be banging their heads on the roof. We could have started with the bonny weather yesterday but it was Candlemas and we know how special that is."

Thord did not envy his mother that job. He had watched his mother and Lina do that before. They had to take the big caisies into the byre, fill them up with dung, hoist them up onto one another's back and carry them out to the fields. Then they would dump the load out and come back for some more. An endless job it seemed.

And that was not the end of the business. After they had carted all the muck out it would have to be spread and his mother and Lina would do that too. They had to have it all finished before his father started ploughing and he would start in March likely so there was not so much time to get it all done.

His mother and Lina got up and went out chattering together to fetch the big caisies. Thord ate his bursteen with as little water as he could manage. He was scooping up the last when his mother and Lina came back, their backs covered with thick straw fletties to protect them from the dung, and went into the byre.

"Oh, gracious!" he heard his mother say. "I think this stuff is even harder than usual, Lina. We'll have a right job hacking at it."

The dung was mixed with the ashes from the fire. They were raked out through a hole in the back and carried through to the byre all winter. There was a little

hole in the end of the byre and any liquid ran off through that so when the ash was added it packed what was left hard and it was dry for the kye to lie on. But it did make it a tough job to cart it out.

"It's like stone, this is," grumbled Lina. "We'll only get it out in spoonfuls."

"Oh, it will not be as bad as that," his mother said and he heard her chuckle.

"Come on, boy," said his father, "or we'll miss the best of the day."

Thord went into the stable and fetched out his favourite horse, Hal. It was such a fine day that he did not want Hal to miss it, standing inside. Hal evidently thought it was a fine day too for he kicked up his heels and almost knocked Thord over.

"What did you take Hal for, Dod?" asked his father. "He will just go daft. It's no distance to the mill. We will be better carrying the corn ourselves."

"Oh, no, please, faither," said Thord. "Hal will be all right in a minute."

Thord spoke sternly to Hal, telling him that he would get stuck back in the stable if he did not behave himself. Hal shook his head but he must have thought that he would miss his chance of getting out for he stopped jumping about and stood quietly while father put on the clibber saddle. A straw mat called a flettie was laid on Hal's back first so that the wooden clibber would not hurt him. Then Thord held one of the wooden sides and father slotted the other one into it and fastened it with a wooden pin across.

"Tie Hal to the post there till we fill the half-fletts," said father.

Thord carried the long straw baskets over to the grain baskets and his father filled them up. He laid some straw over the top of the grain and used a rope to tie the edges of the half-fletts as tight as he could. They carried them outside and fetched two nets made of straw called mezzies to put on the saddle. These were wide at the top where they were fastened to the saddle. They had three corners so one corner hung down to the ground. Father lifted the half-fletts onto the mezzies and took hold of the corner at one side.

"We have to lift both mezzies at the same time," said father, "or the saddle will slip round and the whole thing will fall on the ground. Do you think you can lift one now?"

Thord had never tried to lift anything as big as this yet. His mother had always lifted the other mezzie but she was away out to the field.

"I'm nine now," he thought. "Of course I can lift it."

So he said "Yes!" to his father and hoped that he would not let it drop. It was a real struggle but he did his best. He was a bit glad though that his father reached over the top and hauled it the last bit. "Oh, my!" he thought. "Of course I can do it. I'm nine now."

They set off up along the burn to the Mill. The ducks were having a great time guddling in the burn for worms, he thought. He could see their tails sticking up out of the water. And he could hear a lark singing high up in the air.

"Faither," he said. "It will be all right now, will it not?"

"What will be all right now?" asked his father.

"The lavro singing," he said. "She'll not start to greet now, will she?"

"No, no, Dod," said his father. "I think she will be fine now."

They reached the Mill and found the miller standing outside sunning himself.

"Morning," he said. "What a grand day! It's like Voar already!"

Father and the miller untied the mezzies and lifted the half-fletts off them and laid them inside the door of the Mill.

"Can I leave them here for you to do while I go back and get the meal-cubbies to carry the meal back in," said father. "Dod will give you a hand. He was nine yesterday so he will be well able to help you now!"

"Sure," said the miller. "We'll manage fine." He pulled the lever to make the water run through the mill, opened the first half-flett and started pouring the grain into the hole and through the millstones. Thord had watched him many a time but it was great being allowed to help him.

"Don't let the grain run in too fast," said the miller. "It must go in nice and steady to make sure that it grinds properly."

They had done quite a bit by the time his father came back with the meal-cubbies.

"It would be no use trying to carry the meal home in a half-flett," thought Thord. "It would just trickle out through the sides and there would be a trail all the way home and maybe the lavro or the ducks would get a feed but we would not. And that would make Christane right mad, would it not!"

It was taking a long time to grind all the grain and Thord was beginning to get hungry, but he did not want to admit it as his father and the miller had not said anything about being hungry and he thought he was a worker just like them now. He said nothing and hoped his stomach would not rumble.

"Well, now," said his father with a laugh in his voice. "It's a wonder nobody is hungry with all this hard work."

Thord looked up quickly. His father laughed and took three bannocks and butter out of one of the meal-cubbies. Thord's stomach did begin to rumble and his father and the miller laughed even more at him. His bannock and butter tasted really good though, and he worked even harder after eating it. Father began to scoop the meal into the cubbies and at long last they found that they had emptied both half-fletts and all the grain was ground.

His father filled up the miller's measure, which paid him for his work. Then he covered the meal with straw, pulled the top of the meal-cubbies as tight together as he could and he and the miller loaded them onto the mezzies on the saddle for the journey home.

When they got home with the meal, they found that mother and Lina had finished carting out dung for the day and had begun to make the evening meal. Lina was pounding grain in the knockeen-stone. She was letting Christane try every now and then, so when Christane saw her father come in she shouted, "Look, faither. I'm making the dinner today."

"I'm sorry," said mother. "It's just kale and knockit corn again, with some bannocks and cheese. We've been carrying out the dung all day and we don't seem to have made any difference to the heap!"

Father stuck his head round the byre door.

"Not true," he said. "There's a whole pile of it gone. You have done a lot."

"Not as much as I would have liked," said mother. "But I have been a bit worried about Da. He's been coughing a lot. It's the Axes that he's got, I'm sure. I must make a drink for him right now."

She went to the ale kirn and filled a bowl with ale. She set this almost in the fire to heat up and went into the sallur to fetch some of her store of dried herbs. Thord knew that she would be getting some axes-girse among others. The priest had once told him that axes-girse was called 'dandelion' and that this meant 'lion's teeth'. A lion was a huge yellow animal that lived in a hot country. So why would its teeth be here? Very strange. Sometimes the priest's stories were almost as good as Da's.

When she judged that the ale was warm enough and that the herbs and plants had been thoroughly steeped, mother asked Thord to fetch the sieve so that she could strain it for grandfather to drink. Thord found the sieve and rattled his fingers over it like a drum. It was made of sheepskin with lots of tiny holes bored in it and it made a nice sound. When the ale had been strained through it mother gave it back to Thord to throw the used herbs outside.

"Go and play your drum outside the door," she said.

"I'll need that sieve tomorrow," said father, "to put the meal through before we store it."

"It will be dry again tomorrow," said mother.

Grandfather enjoyed his drink. And he ate a good meal, so mother was not too worried about him.

"Well, now," he said. "After that fine drink maybe you would like a fine story, do you think?"

"Yes, please," shouted Thord and Christane.

"Maybe tonight we'll have the story of the Rousay princess. It's a good one."

"Peerie-Fool, Peerie-Fool," shouted Christane. "I like Peerie-Fool."

"You like Peerie-Fool because he's got a yellow head like you have," said Thord. But he liked Peerie-Fool too, so he said no more.

"Look what I have for you while you listen," said mother. She gave them each a bit of bannock with honey from the big jar. "Some for you too, Da," she said. "It will help your cough."

"Da," said Christane seriously. "Do you think you will cough a lot this year?" She smiled down at the bannock in her hands. Grandfather almost choked on his bannock and honey.

"Now look what you've done," scolded mother and she gave grandfather her bit.

Thord thought that this day had been almost as good as yesterday. There was no reestit mutton but there was bannock and honey, a cosy fire to sit round and Da about to tell a story when he recovered from choking. Lina was helping father tonight to wind some ropes. Sometimes they made straw ropes for tying down the skroos or the roof or lots of other things. Tonight they were making a stronger rope for harness from horsehair.

"Bet that's some of Hal's," thought Thord. "It would be the best."

Suddenly there was a wail from Christane.

"Mam, Mam," yelled Christane, "Ben's eaten my bannock and honey."

Sure enough, there was the dog, licking his lips and looking guilty, but Thord did wonder how much of the bannock had been left. He knew Christane fine. He was sure she would have eaten most of it.

"Here, buddo," said father, "you can have the rest of mine."

"Mm-hmm," thought Thord.

Grandfather had recovered. "Once, a long time ago," he began, "there was a king and queen who lived in Rousay and they had three daughters. They had a grand house to live in and lots of good things to eat."

"So!" thought Thord. "Just like us, then."

Thursday, 4th March, 1557

Thord wakened up early. It felt warm and cosy in the bed and Christane was still sound asleep and not wriggling about beside him. He could hear no sounds at all so he thought it must be very early. There was a little light coming through the sallur door so it must be nearly daylight. There was something wrong, though. Something was missing. And then he realised. The wind had stopped howling round the house. It must be a calm day.

He looked to see if his father was still asleep but he was not in his bed. His mother was just stretching her arms and rising to her feet. Where was his father?

He heard someone at the outer door and then he heard the hens up on the hallans above the entrance clucking to themselves and flapping their wings. A goose hissed as someone came past it and he heard his mother say, "Is the plough all right then? Did you get the pins in again?"

"Everything's fine," said his father. "I found the right bit of wool, from the ewe that had the twin lambs, and the hair from Sholma's tail and I took a hair from the mare. I pushed the markal pin in on top of all that, so I think we'll do fine. I just need to find the dian-stone and we're set."

"I'll get the breakfast ready then," said his mother, "and I suppose you will want to take something to eat with you out to the field."

"Well, it's such a grand day that it would be better to take something with us and then we can keep on with the work. I'll go and waken Dod."

Thord was excited. A whole day spent out in the fields helping his father! He had spent some days last week with the priest learning to read and write. He liked Father Harald but he could not see the point of learning letters and numbers. What use would they be to him? His father could read and write a little but he never did any of it. They had no books at home in any case. And they did not need any books because they had Da. He was better than any book. Far better than Father Harald's ones. Besides, Da told his stories in Thord's own language, the Norn. He found it more difficult to understand Father Harald's stories for they were written in Scots and Thord was only beginning to learn Scots.

Osla had calved so there was plenty of milk to put on his bursteen and to drink as well.

"Thank goodness we have cheese again," said his mother. "You can take the peerie cubbie for the bannocks and cheese and some of the mutton we had yesterday. And I'll give you some bland to drink."

Thord was delighted. He loved bland. Mother made some in a wooden tub after she had kirned the butter. He liked buttermilk too, but bland was extra special. It was clear and pale gold and sparkly. He thought it was strange how you could turn something ordinary like buttermilk into something special just by adding hot stones and then leaving it in a cask for a while.

After breakfast he followed his father out to the stable and they led out the oxen, all four of them. It needed all four to haul the plough as their feet were small and they

sometimes could not get a good grip on the ground. He helped father to yoke them in a row, four abreast. Broad-band, father called it. Then they went to fetch the plough.

They led the oxen out to the field and father carried the plough over his shoulder. Thord wondered why the plough was so light. Surely it would stick into the ground better if it were a bit heavier.

"Faither," he said, "why do you not make the plough heavier to stick in the ground, like the harrows?"

"Well, Dod," said father, "if I did that I would never get it through the earth. The oxen can't pull anything heavier and I couldn't lift it if it got stuck. But it's heavy enough when it goes in anyway, for it has my weight on top of it as well."

"Did you find the dian-stone?" asked Thord.

"Yes, I found it," said father and he showed Thord the little red stone threaded with a rope made from the mare's tail.

"I'll tell you what we don't have, though," he said.

"What's that?"

"We don't have the cubbie with the bannocks. Run back and get it before we go any further."

Thord ran back to the house. He met his mother coming across towards him with the cubbie in her hand.

"I thought I had better come with this before Christane got her hands on it," she said. "I hope all goes well with the plough. Don't forget anything else now or it will likely bring bad luck."

They reached the field that the oats were grown in. No dung had been spread here. This field and the others near it were the outer fields. The cattle were put out here late in the year. Sometimes they could take hay off them and sometimes they were left empty. Da said that they used to cut turf here to put on the roof.

"Why do we always grow oats in these fields, faither?" asked Thord.

"Well, the land here is not so good as the inner fields. We don't put any dung on it and it would not grow bere. But oats will grow in poor land and still give us a good crop."

"I like things made with oatmeal," said Thord. "It's really good."

"Yes, very good, and we use it to make ale as well. It makes good ale. And the straw is great for making things with. It's long and strong and doesn't get flattened with the wind like bere straw. Bere straw is too soft to make things with. And the animals won't eat it. They'll eat oat straw."

"Why don't we grow more then?"

"Well, we don't get a lot of them on a field. Not like bere. We can grow a lot more bere on the same amount of land, so we just grow what we need."

Father lined up the oxen at the end of the field. He fastened on the plough and said to Thord, "You're the pirren, Dod. Off you go."

Thord, the pirren, stood facing the oxen and started to walk backwards slowly, calling them towards him. The oxen strained at the harness and tried to get a grip on the ground. With a final heave they got underway and Thord saw his father lean heavily sideways on the plough and the earth begin to curve up into a furrow. Thord kept walking steadily backwards.

He could hear a lark singing its heart out up in the sky. There was a flock of lapwings drumming their way across the field and a shalder shot up from behind him with a loud cry. He walked backwards. What was that story the priest was telling him last week? Something about walking backwards? Now he remembered. You had to walk backwards out of the room if the king was in it. Or in Scotland I suppose it would be Queen Mary, he thought. What a laugh if you tripped and fell on your backside! What would all the people say? And just with that he tripped over a tussock of grass and fell with a thud.

He scrambled to his feet, worried in case the oxen would walk over him, but of course they had stopped when he disappeared downwards and his father was asking what was happening. "Sorry! I fell," he said.

"Are you all right?" said his father.

"Fine!"

"We're nearly at the end of the field. Watch out for the bank."

Thord glanced behind him and saw the remains of the mound of earth left from last year. He stopped and helped his father to turn the oxen. His father lifted the plough and took it over to the bank. He knocked the earth that was stuck to it onto last year's mound. Next year that would have to be spread back onto the field again before it was ploughed.

They began again, but before his father put the plough into the ground he flipped the dian-stone, which was hung on it over to the other side.

"Why do you do that?" asked Thord.

"It has to be at the sun side always to make sure that the sun shines on the crop and we get a good hairst," said his father.

"How do you know where to put it?" asked Thord. "There's no sun today so you can't know which is the sun side."

"I always know which is the sun side," replied his father. "Even when it's raining."

They went back and fore through the field a good number of times. Thord was beginning to find that his legs were getting sore as they were not used to walking backwards for this length of time. He wondered if he could ask his father to let him rest for a bit, but decided that he could not do that. He was nine now, so he could do anything. Just when he was beginning to think that after all he might not be able to do everything even though he was nine his father called out to him that they would stop at the end of the next furrow to give the oxen a rest.

"Give them a rest?" thought Thord. "They're walking frontwards. I'll bet they would have sore legs if they were going backwards all the time."

Father knocked the plough on the mound, laid it down and said that he thought they had all earned a rest and something to eat. There was a little grass on the end of the field and the oxen seemed quite happy with that. Thord fetched the cubbie, feeling weird at walking forward for a change.

"How's the pirren?" asked father.

"Fine!" said Thord.

The extra special bland tasted extra good.

His father lay down on his back after he had eaten and said he would rest for a few minutes more. Thord knew that his back would probably be aching with leaning on the plough so hard. This was the first day of ploughing and he would feel his back a bit sore. Just like the pirren's legs were a bit sore. But the pirren's legs would get better quicker if he ran about.

Thord ran over to the side of the field and looked in the big ditch there. With luck he might find a toad. He could take it home and frighten Christane with it.

Or an eel! That would be even better. He had no luck however. There was nothing in the water in the bottom of the ditch and he was lucky that he had not fallen in it. He had nearly slipped down the side. It was still too cold to go barefoot and soggy wet rivlins would be pretty bad to walk backwards in.

The weather was being kind to them. Although the sun was not shining and there was a lot of cloud, it was not raining and the day was calm. There was no biting wind to fight against. Father was determined to do as much as he could. Back and fore they trudged and the pirren thought that he did very well. He fell only once more and was still walking manfully backwards when the light began to fail and father thought they should go home.

By this time Thord was really tired and wondered if he could stay awake long enough to get home. His father pushed him in through the door of the house and said he would put away the plough and the oxen himself. Thord stumbled into the dark warm firehouse. His mother fetched him a bowl of broth and a bannock and cheese.

"Do you want a drink of buttermilk, Dod?" she asked.

"Can I have some more bland?" asked Thord.

"Yes, you can. I expect you deserve it. And there's beesmilk pudding for after that."

Thord brightened up. Beesmilk pudding was a real treat which you could only have when a cow had just calved. He gulped down his broth, wiped his bowl with the last of his bannock and held it out again. Lina came over with the pudding.

"I've been working all day at that," she grumbled. "It takes a lot of doing."

"Oh, nonsense," said mother. "It cooked itself in the dish in the big pot of water. All you had to do was make sure it didn't boil dry. Do you want some honey with it, Dod?"

"Me too! Me too!" cried Christane.

"How's the pirren?" asked grandfather.

"Fine!" said Thord.

"How many times did you fall over?"

"I didn't fall over!" said Thord indignantly. "At least, I only fell over twice."

"Only twice? I fell over a lot more than that when I was the pirren," said grandfather.

Thord could not imagine his grandfather walking backwards. Let alone falling over. He looked at him in astonishment.

"Anyway," said grandfather, "your father fell over a lot more than me."

Thord burst out laughing. He could see his father falling over much more easily than he could see Da.

"I want a story, Da," said Christane. She was feeling a bit annoyed because Thord had had a day out with father and now was getting all the attention from Da.

"A story," said Da. "Right. I'll tell you a story about a trow. And this trow lived in the ditch right beside the field that the oats are in."

"Oh, gosh," said Thord. "Is he still there?"

"He might be," said grandfather. "Did you see him, Dod?"

"Well, no," said Thord, "but I was looking in the ditch to see what I could find and I nearly fell in."

"Well, it's a good job you didn't," said Da. "The trow might have got you."

Thord listened as grandfather told the story of the trow and how he had tried to get hold of the dian-stone from the plough.

"But the rope was made of horse-hair and that stopped him taking hold of it. He didn't like horses so the stone was safe."

"Is that why the rope is made of horse-hair?" asked Thord.

"Very likely," said Da.

Tuesday, 16th March, 1557

Thord wakened early. The rest of the family were still asleep and the daylight was just beginning to filter through the liora in the firehouse. He listened for the wind, or worse still for the rain. They were going to harrow the fields they had ploughed to make them ready for sowing. He would be the pirren again and he was sure he would not fall over this time.

He could hear no rain, but there was a little wind rustling in the thatch of the roof. They had a good roof on the house now. He remembered last winter how much it had leaked. The liora always leaked a little with the rain. It was as well to stay clear of it, and in no way to stand under it, when it was raining. You could get soaking wet at the very least and probably black too from the soot it washed down with it. But the leaks from the roof were difficult to avoid. You never knew when a big black drop would land on your nose.

His father had taken the whole roof off, all of the old heather and straw, and had spread it all on the fields along with the dung. It had crumbled to a grey-black dust and had drifted like smoke along the ground. It would help the crops to grow, he had said, and he might have been right at that, because they had had good crops last year.

Then they had had to put the new roof on and it was lucky that it did not rain in the time. Da had helped to make simmons, straw ropes, to hold it all down and it was a very good roof. The hens had stopped looking miserable on their hallans and the spiders seemed to like it too. "Ettercap", he thought. "I like to watch him spin his thread." He lay on his back watching as the light grew stronger and sure enough, ettercap began a web above his head.

His mother rose and went through to the firehouse to waken Lina and start making the breakfast for them all. They were having to be careful now with the meal and grain and not use too much so that it would last until the new crop. They had enough and Da said they were lucky. Some folk were almost starving before the next crop ripened. There was milk to drink, though, and butter and cheese so there was plenty really. Christane complained because she thought she was not getting enough bursteen. "I think if she had a tub full she would still want more," thought Thord.

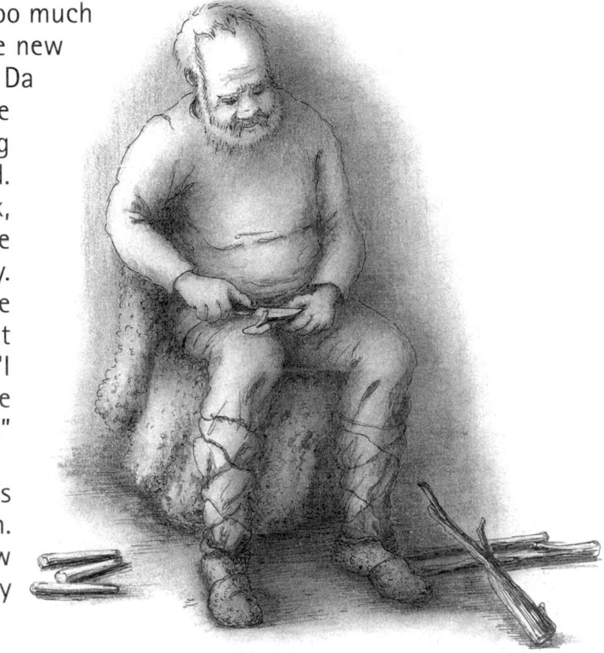

Thord went out with his father to yoke the oxen again. This time the wooden harrow was harnessed and a big heavy flagstone was laid on top.

"Carry the caisie with the teeth, Dod," said father. Thord lifted up the caisie full of teeth, which his father and grandfather had spent many evenings in winter carving. He carried it out to the field after his father and laid it at one side in readiness. He saw his mother and Lina come across the land towards them carrying eetches on their shoulders. These had wooden handles with an iron end put on them. 'A bit like father's axe,' thought Thord, 'but a lot smaller.' Father used his axe sometimes, to cut through straw bundles to make them even, or to cut the heather roots.

The eetches were new. Grandfather thought they would be no use.

"What is wrong with the old eetches with the stones on the end?" he asked.

"Well," said father, "I was told that they would break up the clods of earth much quicker and easier, so I thought we should try them."

So mother and Lina were going to try them out. They were looking forward to it. Mother was sure that the sharp edge of the iron head would chop up the clods easily.

Thord stood facing the oxen. His father climbed onto the flagstone on the harrow. His mother and Lina stood like warriors with axes behind him ready to do battle with the land. "Off you go then, Dod," said his father, and Thord began his accustomed walk backwards, hoping as usual that he would not trip and fall. He watched his father sail along behind the oxen like a skipper on a ship. It looked so much fun and he would like to have tried it but he knew very well that it was more difficult than it looked.

His mother and Lina began banging at the lumps of earth left by the harrows and soon he could see a smooth track where the oxen had passed. 'Like a path from the moon on the loch on a calm night,' thought Thord. He walked carefully backwards to the end of the field. His father turned the harrow around and waited for his mother and Lina to catch up.

"Well," said his father when mother and Lina reached the end. "What do you think?"

"Much better," said mother. "Who is going to tell Da?"

"Ah, well," said father. "Time enough for that when we've finished."

The oxen plodded their calm and slow way back and fore through the field and gradually the moon-path widened and swallowed up the land. Mother straightened up with a hand to her back.

"I'll make a start for home and get the dinner ready. I declare with this new eetch Lina can manage the rest herself," she said. Lina grumbled but nobody said anything. They were all too used to hearing Lina grumble away. It was just another sound in the day like the wind or the bird-song.

"Come on, Dod," said father suddenly, grinning at him. "Let's change places. I'll be the pirren and you can try and stand on the harrow. We're on the last bit now."

"Great," thought Thord. He scrambled round to the harrow while his father ambled round to the front of the beasts. Up on the flagstone he climbed and stood there proudly, trying to look old and capable.

His father called to the oxen and off they set. The harrow jerked forward, Thord wobbled wildly and fell off. His father laughed but did not stop so Thord got up, shook himself and hurried after the harrow. It was difficult to climb on a moving harrow but somehow he managed it and staggered to his feet. Swaying back and fore he tried desperately to stay on the flagstone, expecting at any moment that he would fall off again.

In some strange fashion he found himself after a time still on board and gradually the wobbles in his legs steadied and he stood upright. Frowning to himself he practised this new skill and then began to enjoy it.

"Look, faither," he shouted. "I'm the captain of the ship now." He folded his arms to show off and then realised he should not have done that. He fell off once more and father laughed even louder. Thord laughed too and scrambled back on again. They reached the end of the field and Thord managed to stay on the flagstone when the oxen stopped, so he was quite proud of himself and thought he would tell Da that his father had been the pirren most of the day. Then he thought he had better not. His father would say nothing but Lina would tell his grandfather the truth. Lina always told the truth, even if it would have been better if she had said nothing.

They plodded home to the sound of Lina grumbling away. She admitted that the new eetch broke up the clods more easily but complained that it was heavier and more awkward to use because you had to make sure to hit the right way with it. Father might have been upset about this but mother had said that the new eetch was the best she had ever used so he thought very likely Lina just wanted to complain about something for the sake of complaining.

When they had put the oxen inside and fed them and the rest of the animals they went in to hear what Da was going to say about the new eetch.

"Ingirid was telling me that the new eetches worked well," said Da. "You know, I was sure they would be a great success. That sharp edge would be a great help."

Thord and his father stopped in their tracks and stared at him. Then Thord heard his father laugh out loud.

"You did not!" he said. "You said they would be useless."

"Oh, maybe I did," said Da. "But I thought it was a good idea to try something new and you see I am right."

They sat round the fire and ate their dinner. Thord was pleased that they had finished the field because he could hear the wind rising again and whistling in the liora. It felt so cosy sitting here listening to the wind rising and the cattle moving in the byre and an occasional thump from the stable from Hal.

"Voar is here," said Da, "but winter still has a blow or two to strike yet. And I will tell you why.

"There are many strange things that you can find under the waves in the sea. There are mermaids in the sea and huge whales and strange fish, not like the haddock and cod and the sillocks that we eat but huge fish with big teeth. And there are funny things with long legs like the squid we catch sometimes but much bigger. It is a whole new world down there, a magic kingdom with treasure to be found among the waving leaves of the red-ware and the long lines of droo.

"And in that world there lives a monster, a monster called Teran. He is a horrible sight to look at. He has long, brown, wild hair that waves around his head and staring eyes. His hands and arms are like flippers with great claws on them and his feet are webbed like a duck's but a lot bigger. He roars round the sea in the winter making the wind howl and the waves crash.

"Sometimes you think he is never going to stop and that the sea will be wild for ever and nobody will be able to fish or catch lobsters.

"And then one day in March the Mither o the Sea wakes up and sees what

Teran is doing to her kingdom. She sees the waves crashing and the ducks and auks hardly able to swim and dive in the water.

"This makes her very angry. She decides that Teran must be shut up in a cave before he can do more harm. And so she goes to find him and shut him up.

"But Teran does not want to be shut up in a cave. He is having too much fun, raging around and annoying all the sea-birds and hurling the fish and lobsters around among the ware. He won't do what he is told.

"So there is a huge battle. Teran and the Sea Mither fight and the waves are higher than ever and the sea looks as if it is boiling. This is the Voar Struggle, what we call the Voar Tullyie. Every March this happens and sometimes it is a day or two and sometimes it is a week or two. But the battle will rage without fail in March, and so you can see that we have some wild weather yet to come.

"But then the Sea Mither gets the upper hand and Teran is shut up in the cave and the wind dies down, the waves go away and the sea becomes flat and calm. The summer comes and the sea sparkles in the sun. The ducks splash about and the auks dive down deep in the water. The ware grows big again and the sillocks play dickie-doo among the leaves. The lobsters crawl out of their holes and the crabs run around sideways. The droo grows long lines to reach up through the water to the sun. These are Loki's lines and if you don't take care he will catch your oar and pull you under.

"All summer the Sea Mither looks after the fish and the birds and everything that lives in the sea or that swims or floats on the surface.

"But she gets tired and when autumn comes Teran sees his chance and in September he challenges the Mither o the Sea and there is another great battle. This is the Autumn uproar. We call it the Gore Vellyie and it can be much worse than the Voar battle. This is because the Sea Mither does not want Teran to take over her kingdom again but in the end he wins because she is so tired. So she goes away to rest until the Voar but sometimes in winter she will waken and help the fishermen if they are in trouble.

"And in the Voar, back she comes. I know fine she is coming back now. Soon there will be a big fight again. And who will win?"

"The Mither o the Sea," shouted Thord and Christane together.

Thord went to bed with the beginning of the battle sounding in the liora and the thatch of the roof. He was not worried. He knew who would win.

Wednesday, 17th March, 1557 - Bogel Day

Thord woke the next morning with the sound of the wind moaning in the liora. It was not a really strong wind, not a gale. It was more of a complaining wind, a bit like Lina, he thought. He listened carefully to see if he could hear any rain but there was no sound of it. He did not think there was enough wind to blow away the soil that they had harrowed yesterday.

He heard his mother raking out the fire and grandfather asking someone if they would shift the skylan board as the wind had veered round. He heard the rattle of the board being shifted and Da coughing and saying that that was much better.

When he went through to the firehouse his mother was beginning to make bursteen for breakfast and Lina was using the quern-stones again to grind more bere.

"It's Bogel Day," said his mother. "We need to grind the corn that was grown on the Bogel field today and make some bannocks for supper. And we'll have some chunks of ham too. It will make a fine change."

"You and I have some work to do today, too, Dod," said his father. "We must sow some bere on the field we harrowed yesterday, even if it's only a handful. We need to make sure we have good luck with the crops and it's specially lucky to sow some grain today."

The wind was growing stronger when they went out. Thord could see little waves rising on the loch and splashing more and more on the edge of the land. It looked as if any seed that they sowed would just blow away and be no use.

His father fetched a little cubbie and filled it with bere.

"I don't think there's much point in trying to sow a lot today," he said. "We'll just try to get a little in the ground to make sure of our luck."

They walked together out to the field and the wind rose still more. There was a rainy sound in the wind too and black clouds were gathering to the north. Thord thought that it was cold enough for snow to fall. He liked snow in the winter. His father grumbled about it, though not as much as Lina, but he enjoyed it. And when the loch froze, that was fun. It was often thick enough at the edges to hold them up and they could slide across it with straw bound round their rivlins.

Snow in March was not so good though. It was just as cold but it did not stay long and turned to mud on the land. Sometimes too the sheep would start to lamb and they would lose the lambs in the cold. He hoped that it was not going to snow today. Rain was bad enough.

When they reached the field his father set the cubbie on the ground and took a handful out of it.

"It's no use casting this in the proper way," he said. "We'll just have to put it into the ground like we do the seeds for kale or peas and beans."

Thord took a handful too and they both bent down and poked the seeds into the ground as well as they could.

"We'll just do a strip here and try to get in enough bere to make bannocks for next Bogel Day," said father. "And you'll have to remember, Dod, where we put them so that we can hairst them separately."

Thord looked round him very carefully and was sure that he would remember exactly where they had sowed the bere, although he knew that it would look a lot different in the hairst when the whole field would be full of long waving golden stalks. It was on the edge of the field, it was true, but it still might be difficult to find in the hairst.

He was still thinking about this problem when they finished the seed in the cubbie and then he had an idea.

"Wait here, faither," he said and rushed off to the end of the field. He found what he was looking for – two fairly big stones – and carried them back to his father.

"If we put one at each end of the bit we have sowed," he said, "then we can find it in the hairst easily."

He put one stone down where they had started and the other where they had finished.

"There! That's it," he said.

"Hey! Very good, Dod," said father. "We won't make a mistake now."

The rain began as they headed for home. The wind dropped a little as the rain fell and they hurried towards the house as fast as they could.

Mother was busy baking bannocks over the fire when they went inside. Thord gave the geese a wide berth as he went in and kept his legs well out of their way.

"Magnus," said mother. "Would you take down the ham from the couples and cut slices off it for all of us. I'm going to cook it with kale when I finish these bannocks."

Father reached for the ham and lifted it down. He set it on the stone bench beside the water tub, fetched his big knife, the gully, and cut off a lot of slices. Christane watched him with great interest.

"Nice ham," she said. "It has a nice smell."

It did indeed smell good, with a strong smoky smell. Thord was looking forward to the meal.

He helped his father with the animals as usual and today they went through the house, back and fore, as the rain was much heavier. Thord thought of the poor soggy sheep on the hill and hoped that they had found some shelter among the heather.

Lina took a tub and went to milk Osla. When she finished she poured most of the milk into a settling tub so that the cream could rise to the top and they could make butter. Some of the milk was given to Osla's calf and she mixed a little meal into it.

"Extra for Bogel Day," she said.

Mother looked at her.

"I have never heard of that," she said. "I think you've just made that up, Lina. But never mind. The meal will do the calf good."

Thord thought it was fine that the calf was having a special meal just as they were. When the ham was ready and the bannocks had been spread with butter they sat down round the fire as usual feeling warm and dry. They kept as far away from the liora as they could for it was still raining and big drops were splashing down through the hole every now and then. The smoke from the fire kept most of it out but sometimes an extra heavy drop or two would drive past the smoke and hit the floor.

Da was looking carefully at his bannock.

"Do you not like your bannock, Da?" said Christane. "I'll eat it for you if you want."

"No, no, buddo," said Da. "I like it fine. It's no ordinary bannock, this. It's a bursteen brunnie, specially made for Bogel Day and there is no finer food than that."

Christane looked a little disappointed but the brunnies were big and she had a whole one all to herself. She had extra butter on her one too.

"Do you know how the first bursteen brunnie was made?" said Da.

Thord pricked up his ears. This seemed to be a story he had not heard before.

"No, Da, tell us," he said.

"Well, a long time ago there were two women who lived in two houses near to each other. One of them was like your mother here, a fine, kind, clever lady."

"Oh, what nonsense is this now, Da," said mother laughing.

"Not nonsense at all," said Da. "As true as I am sitting here. As I said, one of them was a fine, kind body. But the other one was a mean, stingy thing with a sharp face and a long nose which she used to stick into everybody's business. Her name was Thora.

"The mean one sometimes went into the kind one's house and she would say, 'Oh, Hilda, I have no food left in the house. I don't know what I am going to give the family to eat when they come home.' And Hilda would say, 'I can give you a bit of ham, maybe, or some dried fish.' And so Thora would go off with some ham and feed her family and go back the next day and say, 'I have no meal left to make bannocks.' And all the time she had plenty of her own.

"This went on for a long time. Till one day there came a knock on the door of the mean one's house.

'Oh, dear,' she thought. "That will be Hilda from next door wanting to borrow some meal from me. What will I do?' She thought if she pretended to have the Axes and cough a lot, Hilda would feel sorry for her and fetch her some Axes-drink, so she began to cough and cough and wail that she was feeling ill with the Axes.

"The door opened and in came a little yellow-haired man with a staff in his hand and a caisie on his back. 'I see you are ill,' he said. 'I can help you. I can do your work for you till you're better and make a drink to help your cough.'

"Thora could not believe her luck.

"She said to the little man, 'Oh, if you help me I will be so pleased. I have such a lot of work to do and I don't know how I will manage it on my own.'

"So the little man set to and did all the work. Thora told him all the things she had to do and a lot more as well and he worked from morning till night for days and days. She kept coughing and coughing and thought that this was great! Somebody to do all the work and no need to give him anything for it.

"After two weeks Thora was getting used to this good life and she began to add other jobs and to ask the little man to do more and more. Her cough was getting worse if anything. By this time she really did have a sore throat because she had coughed so much. It was now March and the family had begun the work on the land. Thora should have carted out all the dung from the byre but that was another job that the little man had done.

"The little man said to her that he thought she must be better by now and he had stayed long enough to help her. He would like his payment now for all the help he had given her. He did not want much, he said. Just a few bannocks to put in his caisie to eat on the long walk home.

"Thora was angry. She did not want the little man to go and she did not want to give him any bannocks. So she said to him, 'If that is all the help you can give me, just asking for bannocks when you know I am ill, then you can just go away right now. I never want to see you again.'

"'If that is how you feel,' said the little man, 'then I will go but I can tell you that no luck will come to this house and your family will work for nothing this year and next. They need not bother to sow for nothing will grow.' And he stormed off out of the house. 'Good riddance,' thought Thora, but then she realised that she would have to do all the work again and she coughed all the more.

"There was a knock on Hilda's door and when she went to see who it was, she found a little yellow-haired man standing on the brig-stones. 'Do you need any help?' he asked.

"'No,' said Hilda. 'But you look as though you are very tired and hungry. Come inside and rest yourself and I'll make you something to eat.'

"So the little man sat in the best chair and put his feet up on a stool and Hilda gave him some bannocks and butter and cheese.

"For a while he said nothing because he was too busy eating. And then he fell asleep and slept for a long time. When he woke up the rest of the family had come in from the fields and were eating their supper. Hilda said he could sleep in front of the fire that night so he curled up into a little ball and went to sleep again.

"In the morning when he woke he heard the wind howling and the rain lashing down. Hilda told him that he had better stay that day with them still and see if the weather was better next day. The little man said that he would stay but that he wanted the goodman of the house to come out to the ploughed field with him and take a handful of corn with him. So they went out with some grumbling and the little man put the corn into the earth and told the goodman that luck would be with him in that hairst and for many to come.

"When they got back to the house the little man told Hilda to make some meal for bursteen. When it was ready he made some big bannocks with it and gave some to everyone. They had never tasted anything so good and ate them all up.

"Then the little man said. 'This is Bogel Day and every Bogel Day you must make these bursteen brunnies and eat them all up. And you must sow some corn; even a handful and you will have luck always.

"When they woke the next morning the little man had gone. But later that year they found that he had been right. They had a very fine hairst and a lot of grain. Which was just as well as Thora's hairst was very poor and she kept coming round to borrow some, coughing all the time.

"Well, you know who the little man was, don't you?" said Da.

"Was he a fairy?" asked Thord.

"Of course he was," said Da. "And we must remember to sow some corn and eat bursteen brunnies to keep our luck. Did you sow some today, Dod?"

"Yes," said Thord. "A handful or two."

Friday, 16th April, 1557 – St Magnus Day

When Thord woke up he knew it was a special day. He knew that this was a special day for the whole of Orkney. It was St Magnus Day, it was a holiday and it was Good Friday too. They had fed the kye and the horses extra the day before so that they would not need to feed them this morning. They would be fed in the evening when the day's celebrations were over.

There was no bursteen this morning. Mother and Lina would not do any work either and so they had bannocks and cheese made the day before. There would be some cold meat later which had been cooked yesterday and there would be plenty of ale for Da and father, and bland for Thord and Christane.

When they had finished their bannocks they set off along the messigate to the little kirk beside the sea, father, mother, Lina, Thord and Christane. Da stayed at home as he could not walk so far now. They followed the road for a while along the edge of the loch and then it began to climb upwards. As they reached the top of the brae, they could see in the distance the sea and the line of houses near the kirk. They stood for a little and looked towards the shore. Thord thought he could just make out the big house next to the kirk which belonged to the bishop. It was a huge house and there were the remains next to it of what had been a palace long ago, so Da said. There was nothing left but crumbling walls now.

There was a large stone on the top of the brae where they were standing. Thord knew that it was one of the Magnus Stones. It was the last stone on which the saint's body had rested before the final part of the journey from Egilsay, where he was killed, to the Birsay kirk where he was buried. The procession would wind its way up to here in the afternoon. Thord could see why those who had carried St Magnus's body had rested here. You could see all round from here and especially you could see for the first time the little kirk.

The road wound down towards the kirk and Thord ran ahead, leaping in the air, turning back to the rest and shouting "Come on! Hurry up!" His father told him to wait a little and he turned aside and pointed to the side of the road. There, beside the messigate, was a well of clear water.

"This is St Magnus well," said father. "This is where they washed his body before they took it to the kirk. See how clear the water is!" Thord looked into the well, watching the water glint on the surface. He suddenly felt thirsty.

"Can I have a drink from the well, faither," he said. "I'm thirsty."

"Yes, of course," said father. "We can all have a drink."

They bent down and used their hands as cups. The water tasted sweet and fresh.

When they reached the shore, they passed the great house of the bishop, called Mons Bellus, and the ruined walls next to it. They went into the kirk and found that there were a great many people already there. Father Harald was pleased to see so many. They crowded into the kirk and listened to Father Harald telling them about the life of St Magnus and the many miracles that had happened to people when they prayed to him. A woman who had been blind could see again. A man who was crippled could walk again. A man and a woman who had no children prayed to St Magnus and he sent them a son.

Thord and Christane liked all these stories very much. They sat and gazed at all the candles burning brightly and giving off as much light nearly as the sun outside. They could see the sun shining through the tiny windows high up near the roof of the kirk. This was often the only light in the kirk, as the priest could not burn candles all the time. Thord had asked Father Harald why the windows were so high up. Father Harald told him that they were high up so that you would look up high towards God to see the light.

"Our house is a bit like that, too," thought Thord. "The liora is the only window that we have but it is high up too so that we have to look up at God. Or we are supposed to. Christane looks down most of the time, at her food."

When the service was over they came out again into the bright sun, blinking their eyes, for after all, although the candles were bright, they were not as bright as the sun.

Father stood talking to some of the men about the weather and when it would be warm enough to sow grain. Father did not think it would be warm enough for a week or two yet. They would have to wait and see. Mother was talking to some of the women about eggs and chickens and baby geese. Christane had found another little girl about the same age as herself and they were playing a game of jumping over the tussocks of last year's dried grass. Thord found Olaf.

"We've lost a lamb," said Olaf.

"What happened to it?" asked Thord.

"An eagle took it," said Olaf. "Faither was up in the hill at the sheep when he saw the eagle come down and take it. It's not the first one, either."

Father came over to them and asked them if they were ready to join in the procession. The priest would lead it and they would walk first to the shore opposite the brough of Birsay. If the tide was right, they might go across to the brough to the little kirk there. Last year the tide had been too high and the procession could not get across. The brough was an important place. It was where St Magnus's body was taken first after he was murdered in Egilsay. Afterwards his body was taken to his own kirk in Kirkwall.

Thord knew that there was a great cathedral called St Magnus Cathedral in Kirkwall. That was a long way from here and they could not walk there. One year, when Thord was small, father and mother had left him with Da and travelled to Kirkwall on a pilgrimage to St Magnus. His bones were in the cathedral and they had gone to see them. Mother had brought back a pilgrim's cross made of lead, the cross of St Magnus. She took it with her each year when they went on the procession.

As they started to walk to the brough, Thord looked across at the great house of Mons Bellus.

"This is a right big place, faither," said Thord. "Is the cathedral of St Magnus as big as this?"

"It's a lot bigger, Dod," said father.

"You would think it was reaching right up to the sky. Inside it is huge and there are so many windows that you would think the sun was shining inside it. There are great pillars to hold up the roof. And the bishop's voice echoes round the walls. And when there is singing the sound stays with you and doesn't float away on the wind."

"It sounds a strange place," said Thord.

"Strange and wonderful," said father.

The sea sparkled in the sun as they walked along the edge. The priest was carrying a banner, which fluttered in the air and sent the shalders screeching away. He was singing the hymn to St Magnus.

Nobilis
Humilis
Magne martir stabilis
(Renowned, humble, Magnus the martyr, be steadfast)
Et tibi laus redditur
In ecclesia;
O quam felix cernitur
Hinc Orchadia.
(And praise be given to you in the church; O, for this, how fortunate Orkney is seen to be.)

When they got nearer to the brough they could see that the tide was wrong again this year and that they would not be able to cross over. The sea was covering the rocks and there was no way that they could walk across. Thord was disappointed. Olaf had been across last summer with his father. He told Thord about walking across through the middle of the sea.

"It must be a bit like Moses," he said.

"Eh?" said Thord.

"You know! What Father Harald told us? The story about him walking through the middle of the sea. When he was running away from that king."

"Oh, yes! I remember," said Thord. "Maybe I can get faither to take me this summer. What is it like over there?"

"Just a little island. Grass and seabirds. Nothing special. There's some old stones with funny marks on them."

The procession wound its way over the land to Skibbigeo where the fishermen kept their boats. On this feast day of St Magnus, all of the boats were drawn up in the nousts. Thord looked down into the geo and across from where they stood he could see some steps set into the side of the geo, leading down to a well. Father Harald stopped and blessed the boats and they walked on across the fields. As they passed the houses more people came out and joined the procession and they all walked slowly over the land and up towards the brae and the Magnus Stone. They rested there for a short time and then walked down to the well. Then with Father Harald's banner fluttering in the wind before them they walked back to the kirk. Father Harald carried his banner into the kirk and the procession was over.

Some people were already starting to walk home. Olaf and his father went away to visit someone and Father called to Thord to come with him and mother and Christane and Lina to visit their cousin Kettil, the fisherman. Thord went with them into the little smoky house. It had a fire in the middle just like Kirkbuster but it did not have a back like theirs. The fire was on a raised square hearth and it seemed to Thord that the smoke swirled round more than it did at home. The roof was hung with fish, drying and curing in the smoke.

The house smelled differently too. It took Thord a little time to work out why it was different and then he realised that he was missing the smell of the animals. There was just a smell of fish among the peat-reek. There was no byre here. There were lots of other exciting things though. Nets and creels and ropes stacked up against the walls.

Kettil had some food ready for them and Thord was every bit as eager to eat as Christane. The walk had made him hungry and there was still the walk home.

They set off in a little while and Olaf and his father came too. As he walked along the side of the loch, Thord was remembering some of the stories that Da told them. There was one about a monster that lived in the loch. He could not remember its name but he did hope that it would not come out now and catch them all. It would be a pity on a nice day like this.

All the way back along the lochside Thord kept a wary eye out for the monster but perhaps because it was St Magnus Day the monster did not put in an appearance. Thord kept thinking about the procession and the brough. He hoped he could persuade his father to take him to the brough in the summer, but there was another place that he wanted very much to go and see. There was no hope of going there though. But he so much wished he could see the great cathedral of St Magnus.

When they reached home they were all tired and hungry once more. Da was waiting to hear all about the procession and asked how many people had been there. It seemed that there had been lots and lots more people when Da was younger, so many that the procession stretched from the kirk right round the shore and back to the loch.

"That would have made a good feed for the monster," thought Thord.

Lina and mother started to make supper for since the procession was over they could do some work now. Father and Thord went to feed the animals who were glad to see them. Christane went to feed the hens and they could hear her say, "That's for you, Lotta. You can have some more." Lotta was Christane's favourite. She was a big white hen and bossed the others around.

When they were eating their supper, father said, "I think I should take Dod somewhere this summer, maybe in August after the peat-carting and the hay."

"Oh, good," thought Thord. "Maybe the brough!" and he gazed at his father hopefully.

"Yes," said father, "I think we should go to Kirkwall for St Olaf's Fair and he could see the cathedral."

Thord was speechless. He could not believe it. It could not be true.

"That's a good idea," said mother. "You could take some of the extra cloth I have and trade it too. As well as the pen-feathers. Maybe we will have some butter to spare. And you can stay with my sister Freda and her husband. They will be pleased to have you."

"That's settled then," said father. "We can start making some plans."

"I want to go too," said Christane.

"You can't go this time," said mother. "You're too small yet. Wait for a few years."

Christane was not pleased. Her mouth turned down and she scowled.

"I'll bring you a fairing," said Thord when he had got his breath back.

Christane cheered up.

"I want a peerie wooden horsie," she said.

There was no need for Da to tell them a story that night. Thord would have been too excited to listen in any case. He gazed round the fire at all the faces and thought that he must be the luckiest boy alive.

Sunday, 18th April, 1557 - Paese Sunday

It had seemed a long time till Paese Day. Thord had counted off the days with grandfather. Grandfather said,

"First, it comes Candlemas Day
"And then the new moon;
"And then it comes Brose Day
"If it was ever so soon;
"And then there's forty days
"Atween Brose Day and Paese Day -
"The forty days of Lent."

So they had counted them off and waited for Paese Day. St Magnus Day had come and gone and Good Friday with it and now Paese Sunday was here at last. Thord was excited. He knew it was a very special day. And he knew there would be eggs to eat today as well. His mother had been collecting some ready for today. She had set aside a good number for the hens to sit on so there would be chickens later. But there was still plenty for eating.

He heard the geese hiss as someone passed them. They were getting extra fierce now as they were sitting on eggs too. There would be goslings later as well but they were not so much fun to play with. Well, you could not play with them at all for the geese just chased you away and their beaks were not to be argued with. Thord had been bitten by a goose when he was small and wanted to play with the baby geese. He remembered how sore it was and now he stayed well clear of the geese when they were sitting on eggs or had goslings.

He wakened Christane and they ran through to the firehouse to see if breakfast was ready. He found that his mother and Lina had made bursteen and were now boiling eggs in the big pot. He was looking forward to meeting some of the other boys from neighbouring farms after they had all been to the kirk.

This morning they were all going to go to the kirk together, except Da who found it difficult to walk so far now. He loved to go outside in the bonny weather and see what was happening round the farm, but he did not like to go out in the cold because his knees got sore and then they ached for ages. Mother would make him one of her drinks but sometimes even that did not help. Da never complained about it but you could tell when his knees were sore because he limped a bit when he walked.

Thord was busy eating his bursteen when he heard his mother say something very quietly to father. He looked at them and saw his father smiling. "That will be good," he said. His mother looked across at Thord and Christane and said to his father, "The roof's dropping soot." Christane turned her head up to the roof near the liora and looked hard at it. His father burst out laughing and winked at Thord. And suddenly Thord understood what his mother and father meant when they said the roof was dropping soot. They said it often and it had puzzled Thord many times. Of course the roof dropped soot when it was raining but they said it too when there was no rain.

It must mean that there was something they did not want Christane and him to hear. If they said it and Christane looked at the roof, then they would know she was listening and they would wait and speak about it later.

"The roof's not dropping soot, Mam," he heard Christane say.

"Come on," said father. "It's time we were off to the kirk. Father Harald will be watching for us."

They set off beside the loch, along the messigate, to the kirk. Many of their friends were there already and it was fine to speak to them again and to greet some relations that they had not seen since Yule. It was not that they lived so very far away but in the winter months nobody stirred from their own house unless for a special occasion. Now that the windy month of March was nearly at an end there would be a lot more visits between them all.

When the service was over mother and Christane and Lina went back home straight away but father and Thord stayed talking at the kirk a little longer. Thord's cousin Olaf was there. He was a year or so older than Thord but they were good friends when they met.

"Are you coming up the hill later, Dod?" asked Olaf.

"I hope so," said Thord. "Need to fetch my eggs first, though."

He and father went home. Thord's boiled eggs were ready for him in a little cubbie and he picked them up and went outside again. It was a fine day. The sun was shining and there was not much wind. The ground was beginning to dry up so there was no need to tie straw bundles around his rivlins.

His father came outside chuckling to himself.

"Christane is still trying to find out what your mother and I were talking about earlier," he said. Thord had forgotten about it all by now with the excitement of collecting his eggs and the promise of seeing Olaf again up on the hillside.

"What were you speaking about?" he asked.

"Your mother is going to make some very special Paese bannocks and she doesn't want Christane to know about them until they are ready as she will probably eat them as soon as they are made," said his father. "Lina is going to take her for a walk to the brae to roll some eggs. That will give your mother time to bake."

Thord and his father walked back a little along the messigate to meet Olaf and his father. Then they all turned to go up the hill. As they got nearer to the hillside they could see that there were quite a number of men and boys there. Thord ran the last few yards to where Olaf was standing.

"How many eggs have you got?" he asked Olaf.

"I have six," said Olaf. "How many do you have?"

"I've got six," said Thord.

"Come on then," said Olaf. "Let's see whether yours or mine lasts the longest."

He threw up one of his eggs high in the air and it landed with a soft thud on the ground.

"Still whole," shouted Olaf.

Thord threw one of his and it did not break its shell either.

Around them there were lots of boys throwing eggs up as high as they could. Thord noticed one little boy standing at one side, watching and laughing. He was shivering a little as he had only a very thin coat on and although he had rivlins, they were split along the side and he had no socks.

"Hullo!" said Thord. "What's your name?"

"Karl," said the boy.

"Is your faither here with you?" asked Thord.

"No," said Karl. "My faither's dead. There's just me and my Mam. We stay over there in that house."

Thord looked and saw a tiny one-roomed house made from turf. He thought it must be a bit stuffy inside and smoky. He could see a trickle of smoke coming out of the roof but there was no proper liora and no skylan board.

"How many eggs have you got today?" he asked Karl.

"Well," said Karl. "I don't have any with me but I like watching all the others."

"I have plenty," said Thord. "You can have some of mine if you like."

Karl's eyes lit up. Soon he and Thord were throwing their eggs as high as they could and watching carefully for the first signs of the shells breaking.

Olaf joined them. He knew Karl and his mother, as he lived not far from them. Olaf's egg broke first.

"There's one of mine gone," said Olaf and he peeled it and ate it before throwing up the next one. Karl's broke next but he did not peel it. He brought it across to Thord and showed him that it was broken.

"Eat it," said Thord.

"But it's your egg."

"I have more. You can eat your share."

When all the eggs had been eaten it was time to go home again. Thord noticed that Karl had not eaten his last egg and asked him if he was not hungry. Karl said that he was going to take this one home to his mother, as she had not had an egg for Paese. Thord thought of the three he had eaten and the six that Olaf had swallowed and felt a bit mean.

On the way home he asked his father about Karl and his mother.

"Yes, I know them, Dod," said his father. "Your mother sends them meal and cheese when she can and so do other folk. We just forgot about the eggs. It was fine that you gave him some of yours."

"Well," said Thord, "I was really remembering Da's story from Bogel Day. I thought maybe he would turn out to be a fairy so it would be better if I shared with him."

"Oh," said his father, "I think that maybe you would have shared anyway, Dod."

"I don't suppose Christane would have shared even if it was a fairy," said Thord.

Christane had had a fine time with Lina rolling eggs and eating them. She came back to the house carrying the last one in her hand.

"I kept a egg for you, Da," she said and handed it to him.

Da was surprised and delighted.

"She's so full she couldn't eat that one," said Lina.

"Don't spoil it," said Da.

There was kale and reestit mutton for dinner and Thord knew by the twinkle in his mother's eyes that there was more to follow. When the mutton and kale were finished mother rose and went through to the sallur. She came back carrying some thick bannocks.

"I put them through there to hide them so that I could surprise you all," she said. "These are made with the last of the oatmeal. It's a special Paese bannock for you all."

She handed round the bannocks, one each and one left over.

Thord bit into his and thought that he had never tasted anything as good. It was not like the usual bannocks. It was not so crumbly but it was soft and sweet.

"What did you make this with, Mam?" he asked.

"Well," said mother. "I made them with eggs and honey. That's why they are so good."

Thord finished his bannock. He saw Christane looking at the spare bannock hopefully.

"Do you think you could keep that bannock for Karl and his mother?" he asked.

"Oh, this one is for you and Christane. I have one to take to Karl tomorrow with some eggs. Here's your bit Christane," she said, handing her half of it. She gave Thord the other half and he smiled with relief. It was fine thinking about other folk but sometimes it was good to be greedy too, he thought, as he ate his bit.

Da began to tell the story of Paese to them all, as he said there was no other story so good as it on Paese Day. Thord had heard it many times, from Da and from the priest. He thought Da could tell it better.

He fell asleep dreaming of eggs and fairies. It had been a long time through Lent with plain food and just enough of it. Today's feast had been splendid.

Wednesday, 28th April, 1557

The weather had been getting much warmer. Over the last few weeks there had been many sunny days and the grass and the plants were growing well.

Da said that it was proof that the Sea Mither had won her battle and Terran was shut up in his cave for the summer. Da was going outside more often now and he liked to sit outside on a straw stool in the sun in front of the door and next to the bus-herra. He did not sit for a very long time for it was still a little cold. Fresh, mother called it. She would come out and take him inside again if she thought he had been out long enough.

Da still had a cough. It was not much but it made mother anxious still and she kept giving him Axes-drink. She had finished the ale in the kirn early in April and had made some more. It was very good this time. Father had told Thord that they had to say "burn" instead of "water" when they made ale, just as they said "ingle" instead of "fire" when they lit the fire in the kiln. It did not do to use the real words in case the trows heard you. They would cast a spell on the ale or on the grain drying and it would all go wrong. So they had been careful and the ale was good.

Mother went out a lot just now looking for the first plants and leaves to make Axes-drink for Da. It would be a month or two yet before they got very many of them but there were some things growing already, especially axes-girse, and mother said the fresh leaves made a much better drink. Da said so too and his cough was getting better.

This morning the sun was shining brightly and the light was pouring through the liora in a gold stream. The smoke from the peat-fire twisted and shone as it vanished through the liora and there was no need to shift the skylan board. Father and Da were talking about sowing. The field with the oats was ready with a handful or two of extra oats sown over the top. Now they had to think about putting in the bere. This was the most important as they depended on the bere crop for almost all their meal.

While he ate his breakfast father kept going to the door and looking out at the weather. The sun felt warm on Thord's face as he stood in the doorway beside his father looking at the weather too and wondering what he should be looking for.

"I think it might be warm enough," said father. Thord thought it was really warm. Almost warm enough to go without his rivlins. He thought he had better keep them on for a bit yet though. It might turn cold again.

"Well, I'll come and have a look at it," said Da. "Wait till I finish my bursteen."

"What are we looking at, faither?" asked Thord.

"We're going to have a look at the ground, Dod," said father, "just to see if the earth is warm enough yet."

"Oh, so even though it's a bonny day the ground might be cold still?" said Thord.

"That's the way of it," said father. "And we need Da to tell us if it is right. He knows most about it. He can tell if it is warm enough."

"Can you not tell, faither?" asked Thord. He was a bit disappointed as he thought his father knew everything. He could not tell stories like Da could, right enough, but he could do everything else.

"I can guess but Da is best at this and I can learn from him," said father. "Just as you will learn from me in time."

"I can maybe start now and then I can learn from you both," said Thord.

"Indeed that would be the best way of all."

It was too far for Da to go out to the field to look at the ground. They went round to the kale-yard instead. Mother and Lina had already dug the yard and made it ready for kale and peas and broad beans. Once the bere had been sown they would plant the yard. Mother had a store of kale-seed saved and peas and beans. If Christane had not eaten them, thought Thord.

Da pulled down his trousers and sat down on the earth that had been dug over. Father did the same and Thord copied them. The earth felt cold and damp against his bare skin.

"Yes," said Da. "This is warm enough now. You can go ahead."

"Warm enough?" thought Thord. It did not feel at all warm to him. He touched the ground around him glumly. "I must have a lot to learn yet," he said to himself.

"Come on, Dod," said father, pulling up his trousers again. "We need to fetch the cubbies for sowing and load up Hal with the half-fletts with the seed in."

The grains of bere had been steeped in the burn earlier in the month and then they had been spread out in the barn to dry again. This was to make them grow quicker and indeed some of the seeds were already showing little sprouts.

Thord led Hal out of the stable and helped put on the clibber saddle. Mother helped tie on the mezzies and lift the half-fletts with the grain onto them. They set off for the field and Thord was glad to see that Hal was being good. He was picking his way carefully over the land, avoiding rabbit-holes.

They reached the field and unloaded the half-fletts. Father set them at the side of the field and opened them. He filled a cubbie with grain, hung it round his shoulders by its straw rope and stepped out onto the ploughed land. He took a handful in his right hand and swung it from side to side four times as he walked forward. He let a little grain slip through his fingers at each cast and then did the same with his left hand.

"Make four casts with each handful," he said. "You fill your cubbie and try now, Dod." Thord filled his cubbie and walked beside his father trying his hardest to swing as far out and as evenly as he could. His father watched him and said that he was doing fine.

They walked over the field in the bright sunshine listening to the birds calling and the lavro singing its heart out above them. Suddenly its song stopped and Thord saw it drop from the sky like a stone into the grass. He looked up to see what had made it do that and saw, wheeling in the blue sky, a fan of wings spread far above. An eagle, he thought. The rest of the birds were scattering, screeching.

"Look, faither," he pointed, but his father had already seen it. He was watching anxiously to see whether it was heading towards the sheep and the lambs on the hill. Two lambs had been lost already this year, one of them belonging to Olaf's father.

The eagle wheeled away across the loch and father heaved a sigh of relief. The lambs would be safe for today. There were ducklings too on the burn and mother had some chickens. They were near the house all the time and the eagles did not usually come close to the houses and the people. When you saw one though you were worried. There were stories that eagles had carried off babies. Olaf had told him that. Da never told stories like that in case he frightened Christane. It was all right to frighten her with stories of trows and hogboons because you never saw them, but you could often see an eagle, so that was different.

They worked their way steadily along the field and back, filling the seed cubbies every now and then. The first half-flett was almost empty when father stopped and said that they would take a rest now and see if mother had given them any bannocks and butter and cheese. She had remembered and they were in a little cubbie with a lid and there was some bland in a skin bag to drink as well.

It was fine to sit in the sun and eat their bannocks and listen to the birds again. There was no sign of the eagle. Thord saw a little vole run along the field and disappear into a hole. It would have a good supper tonight, he thought, with all the grain they had sown. There would still be plenty left to grow.

They worked away through the afternoon, the sun sliding across the sky in the south and heading towards the west. The second half-flett emptied.

"That's that for today, Dod," said father. "Catch Hal now and we'll go home."

Hal had enjoyed his day out and was not ready to go back to the stable but Thord caught him at last. They tied up the half-fletts and the cubbies with the mezzies and set off for home. When they were nearly at the house they saw mother coming running towards them. Thord could see Olaf behind her and he ran to meet him.

"Have you come for a visit?" he asked.

"Sort of," said Olaf. "My faither has come to see your faither because he's a Lawrightman for this district."

Thord knew his father was a Lawrightman but he did not know why they should want him now. Usually it was only at sheep-shearing time that he was needed. He could hear his mother speaking to his father and thought that he heard something about an eagle. Olaf was tugging at his elbow, looking excited.

"My faither has killed an eagle!" he said proudly.

Olaf's father, Jon, came to meet them.

"I came to you, Magnus," he said, "for you would know what I should do. I managed to kill the one that was taking the lambs, I think. But it's so long since anyone killed one I am not sure what to do now."

"Have you got some of the feathers with you?" asked father.

"Yes, I have them here." Jon produced some brown feathers and a few white ones.

"Now, that's all the proof you need," said father. "I will come with you and we can go round as many houses as we can tonight. Then people can spread the word round."

"What does faither have to go round the houses for?" asked Thord. They had reached the brig-stones in front of the house by now and Da was standing there watching them. He looked at Thord and said, "Jon has the right to a hen from every house in the district because he has killed an eagle. Your father will help him and make sure he gets what is due to him."

"Do we have to give him one too?" asked Thord. "He is a kinsman of ours after all."

"Of course we have to give him one. Think of all the hens and chickens and lambs he will have saved us by what he has done."

Mother went into the house saying that she must get them all something to eat before Magnus and Jon set off to the next house. With Lina's help there was soon some broth and bannocks for everyone and somehow they all found a chair or a stool to sit on. Thord and Christane sat on Da's bed as usual, eating their broth and listening to father asking Jon how he had managed to kill the eagle.

"I was just lucky," said Jon. "Very lucky. Maybe the fairies were helping or something. I was out on the field with Olaf, sowing bere. It's the first day it has been warm enough. We saw the eagle high up flying across the loch and we were glad that it was going away from the lambs. We worked on sowing the field and then I thought we should go and check the snares I had set the night before. I thought maybe we would have caught a rabbit or two. If we checked them on the way home we might have tomorrow's dinner.

"We walked over to the rabbit warren and just as we got there the eagle appeared again. We watched it circling in the sky and then suddenly it dived down near us. I wondered what it had seen so Olaf and I went over to look. It had found a rabbit and it had landed on top of it. I could see that it was trying to take off again but it could not manage it. The rabbit was caught in the snare and the eagle could not lift it. You know when an eagle gets its talons round anything they lock fast and it can't let go again right away. So it could not get up into the air and it could not let go of the rabbit. What made me do it I don't know, but I grabbed up a big stone that was lying beside me and flung it at the bird.

"I was angry at it for it was one of my lambs it had this year. The stone flew out of my hand and I'm sure it must have been the fairies, for it knocked it on the head and killed it. We went over to make sure and it was dead right enough. But it really was just luck. There was nobody more surprised than myself when I hit it. We took it home after we had finished checking the snares and then I thought we had better come to see you."

"I'm glad you did," said father. "Maybe we should go now and we will reach the next house or two before dark yet. There should be some moonlight later. The moon is just a few days past full so there will be a fair bit of light. We can go round a few houses I think."

Father and Jon set out to go to the nearest house. Da told them not to go too near to the loch in the dark or Nuckelavee would maybe get them.

"What's Nuckelavee, Da?" asked Christane.

"It's a horrible monster that lives in the loch and if you go too near the edge it will come out and catch you."

"What will it do to you?" Christane's eyes were as round as the full moon, gazing at Da.

"Maybe eat you," said Da.

"I wouldn't like to be eaten."

Mother came back into the house after waving to Jon and Olaf and father. She looked at Da and said, "We will have to send a hen to Jon tomorrow. I think maybe we should give him the white one." She looked at Da with a twinkle in her eye.

"No, not Lotta," wailed Christane. "You can't give him Lotta." She began to cry, sobbing, "Not Lotta! Not Lotta!"

"You don't think I would let anybody take Lotta, do you?" said Da. "She lays the best eggs and she will have the best chickens this year, just you wait and see." He gave Christane a big hug and sat her on his knee. "We won't let anybody take Lotta."

Thord felt very sleepy. He had spent a whole day walking up and down the field. Then there had been the excitement of Jon and the eagle. But he was determined to stay awake until father came home. An extra special story from Da would keep him awake he thought. He looked across at Da to ask him to tell a really good one and found that Christane was asleep on Da's knee and Da himself had fallen asleep in his warm sheepskin chair. Lina was yawning. And mother was saying that she was going to put Christane to bed and Thord should go too.

"I want to stay up until faither comes home," said Thord.

"He will likely be quite a while, Dod," said his mother. "We should all go to bed and he will be there when we waken in the morning."

Thord fell asleep as soon as he lay down. Mother covered him and Christane with the blankets and went to bed herself. She looked at Thord smiling to himself in his sleep and knew that he was dreaming about the fine day he had had.

Saturday, 1st May, 1557

Thord woke with someone shaking his shoulder. He opened a sleepy eye and peered into the darkness.

"What is it?" he said.

"Sh! It's just me," whispered his father. "It's time to get up if you want to come with Lina and me up the hill to watch the sun rise. It's May morning, Dod. Do you want to come?"

Of course he wanted to go with his father. He crept out of bed carefully so as not to wake Christane and hunted for his rivlins. Mother had said yesterday that she did not want to go and she thought that Christane was still too small so they would stay home with Da and make breakfast for them to have when they got back.

He went through to the firehouse expecting to hear Lina grumbling away about having to get up so early. Father was building up the fire and in the light of that he could see that Lina was not grumbling. She was smiling. How strange.

Da was awake and asking father to fetch him a drink because his throat was dry. He had coughed a bit during the night, he said, but it was nothing to worry about.

"I expect Mam will worry about it all the same," thought Thord.

Lina fetched some bannocks and butter, which had been made ready the night before. They could eat them as they walked up the hill. The three of them said goodbye to Da and set off in the faint light of early morning. They crossed the burn and headed towards the hill where they had thrown up the eggs on Paese Day. This time they had further to go, though, because they had to climb to the top.

Thord was still wondering why Lina was in a good mood. He thought he would ask his father when Lina was not listening. They walked along in the silence. There was no wind and it seemed as if it would be a fine day later. It was not cold. Thord thought that it would not be long before he could go barefoot again as he did each summer. Maybe he could have a new pair of rivlins in the autumn as his feet were growing fast and he did not think these would fit him much longer. They could be kept for Christane.

Light was seeping up into the sky as they reached the side of the hill where they had thrown up the eggs. They could just make out other figures in the half-light climbing upwards. As they neared the top they saw that there were many others waiting there for the sun to rise.

The sky changed from pale yellow through rose pink to blue and suddenly the first rays of the sun hit the top of the hill flooding them with gold. Lina bent down and scooped her hands along the top of the heather. When they were wet with dew she splashed the water on her face and rubbed it in.

"What's she doing that for, faither?" whispered Thord.

"That's what young ladies do on May morning, Dod," said father. "It's to make them beautiful."

"Well, I think Lina will need about a tub full, don't you faither?" said Thord.

"Sh!" said father. "Don't let her hear you say that!"

They watched the sun climbing higher into the sky and the light became stronger round them. The birds began to wheel round them. There were lapwings drumming the air with their wings. A whaap flew by crying mournfully and even on the hilltop the shalders were noisy.

When the sun was well clear of the horizon people began to make their way down the hill again and towards their homes. Thord thought he understood why Lina had been smiling now. She was looking forward to being beautiful. "What will she say when it doesn't work?" thought Thord, for he did not think it would.

The sun was high in the sky when they reached home. Mother had bursteen ready for them and Da was sitting outside the door in the sun, next to the bus-herra as usual.

Christane wanted to know where they had been.

"We've been to the top of the hill to watch the sun rise," said Thord, "because it's May morning."

"I wanted to go," said Christane.

"You're too small yet," said mother. "In a few years you can go."

"What did you do up there?" asked Christane, hoping it was nothing exciting as she had missed it.

"Faither and I just watched the sun rise," said Thord, "but Lina washed her face in the dew off the top of the heather."

"What did she do that for?"

"It's supposed to make her beautiful," said Thord. "I don't think it will work."

"Why not?" asked Christane.

Thord was not sure himself why he was so certain that the dew would not work, so he just said to Christane "Well, it might," and left it at that. He went inside to eat his breakfast

He was just finishing his bursteen when there was a loud yell from Da.

"Come here quick," he heard him shout. They rushed outside to see what was wrong to find Da pointing at the burn. They looked in the direction his finger was pointing and saw Christane struggling to her feet in the water at the edge of the burn. As soon as she saw them all looking at her she burst into tears. The wails got louder and louder until father reached her and lifted her up.

"What happened, buddo?" he said. "Did you trip and fall in the burn?"

"I was wanting to be beautiful, too," said Christane. "There was no water on top of the grass so I had to go to the burn," she sobbed.

"Never mind, buddo," said father. "You'll likely be extra specially beautiful since you've washed a lot more than your face." He carried her to mother who took her inside to dry her and her clothes off.

Lina came through from the byre with the milk pail and emptied the milk into the kirn. She clucked her tongue when she saw Christane.

"What have you been up to?" she asked.

"She's been washing her face in the May dew," said mother, "or rather the May burn. She fell in."

Lina laughed and Christane scowled at her.

"That's the kirn full, ready for kirning," said Lina. "Do you want me to start now?"

"Yes, we can make a start," said mother. "This butter will be for our own use. We have enough for the scat I think."

Lina took the wooden stick and began to plunge it up and down in the kirn. This could take a long time and sometimes they had to take it in turns throughout the whole day. Thord had seen his mother at times exasperated with it and then she would drop a hot stone from the fire into the kirn to make the butter come. At other times it would not take very long at all and you would hear the gurgling

sound of the milk turning to a sharp 'swoosh' as the butter arrived. It was usually better butter if it kirned faster.

Thord took his turn today and Lina told him to turn the stick in his hands each time he pulled it up. It was quite hard work and he was glad to hand over to mother. Today, however, they were lucky and the butter came quite quickly. Mother lifted it out and took it outside to the low wall, which ran along the side of the brig-stones.

She put the butter on the top of the wall. Thord fetched a pail of water from the well and mother ran the water over the butter to wash it. When she thought it was clean enough she began to work the water out of the butter with a wooden spoon and make it into a block. She carried the butter back into the house and through to the sallur to store it. Thord went to help her. He had a special reason for this and he wondered that Christane was not coming too. Then he realised that Christane had been ahead of him. She was already in the sallur.

Mother took the butter over to the big tub that she stored it in. Before she could put it in she had to cover the last lot with honey to keep it for the winter. This lot would be covered in its turn. Thord thought that with any luck there would be a spoon to lick after she was finished. He was right but he had to share with Christane. He got the back to lick while she had the inside of the spoon.

In the firehouse Lina was emptying the kirn into tubs. One large tub was for buttermilk and there was a smaller one set aside for making bland. Mother would drop hot stones into this and leave it to settle. The whey solids would separate and leave a clear liquid. If she put this into a cask and left it, it would become sparkly and be really good. If it stopped sparkling you could add some new stuff and it would be good again. The white solids could be eaten with milk. That was good, too. Or they could be hung up to drip and then they were made into cheese. A lot of things could be made from one lot of kirning.

Mother decided that they would eat the white curds with milk today when she had finished. Thord was pleased, as this was a real treat.

In the evening they sat round the fire as usual eating their supper and trying to coax a story from Da. He did not seem to want to tell one and busied himself with eating his curds and milk. He wanted to know what Thord had thought of the sunrise on the top of the hill and asked him lots of questions. Thord described the changing colours of the sky and how he had thought the golden light when the sun rose the best of all. Finally he told Da that Lina had washed her face in the dew.

"That was a good idea!" said Da.

Mother cleared away their dishes and spoons and sat down again and at long last Da said, "What about a story?"

"Yes, please," shouted Thord and Christane.

Da asked if they had ever heard of the Fin Folk. Thord thought he remembered something about them but it was so long ago since Da had spoken of them that he could not remember properly.

"Well, the Fin Folk have farms just like us," said Da, "only theirs are under the sea. The have kye and sheep and hens too I expect, but they all live at the bottom of the sea."

Christane stared in wonder. "Grass, too?" she asked.

"Well, sea-weed, anyway," said Da.

He began to tell them about the Fin Folk and especially the Fin King and the battle that he fought with the men of Sandwick. The men of Sandwick won in the end which was fine and Thord and Christane went to bed happy.

Monday, 24th May, 1557

The month of May had been warm and dry. Thord and Christane had taken off their rivlins and were now running around with bare feet most of the time. They were spending almost the whole day outside from early morning till the sun started to set at night. Thord spent a day now and then with Father Harald learning to read and write. He was very good at it, Father Harald said, but Thord could still see little point in learning. It was a trick, really, just like walking on your hands or balancing something on your nose. It was fun but not a lot of use in everyday life.

Father had decided that since it had been such good weather they would be able to cut their year's supply of peats and today they were all going to the peat-banks to cut the turf and spread it to dry. Da was not going to come with them but everyone else was going, even Christane.

They got up very early indeed and ate a good breakfast round the fire before they set off, as they would have a long day at the peat-banks. They would be really hungry when they got home even though mother made sure there were bannocks and butter and cheese in a cubbie with something to drink. Da said he would try and make the supper for them and have it ready when they got back.

Thord went with his father and took Hal out of the stable. He was going with them to carry the cubbie and the tusker and probably Christane. One horse would do today but when they had to cart the peats home they would need both horses and they would have to make a great many trips.

They did not have very far to walk to the peat-banks but Thord was enjoying it, watching the birds and listening to their calls. At one point the sky seemed full of whirling black flakes of soot as the lapwings wheeled above them in a dense cloud. Lapwings seemed to like to fly together just as shalders liked to fly on their own.

Christane had not gone very far before she was complaining that her legs were getting sore and father carried her on his shoulders for a little. Mother and Lina were chatting away to each other as they walked, mostly about the other people who lived round about. Thord heard mother say, "Now I don't think you should say that, Lina. You don't know if that's true and it's not a very kind thing to say. I've told you before, if you can't say something nice about somebody, don't say anything at all." Lina grumbled a bit but she knew mother was right.

They reached the peat-banks to find others already there and some of them had started work. "Fine day for it," they all shouted to father as he took the tusker off Hal's back and went to look at the bank. It was fine and dry on the top so he began to flay the bank, taking the top inches with the heather growth and roots off before he started to cut the peats.

The tusker was a bit like a thin spade with a bit sticking out to put your foot on to shove it down. Thord watched as his father cut the rows of peats, the tusker slicing through the ground like a knife through butter. As he cut he lifted them out and tossed them onto the top of the bank to dry out.

There were other children there as well and Thord and Christane played with them for a while, hiding among the banks and shrieking when they were found. Then father called to Thord to come and help him. Lina and mother were laying out the peats in order so that they might dry better and father was cutting quicker than they could set them up. Thord ran across to help and left Christane with her friends.

Father cut another row and then asked Thord if he wanted to try.

"You'll have to learn sometime," said father. "Might as well start now." He handed him the tusker, showed him how to put it into the ground and push on it and then said, "Go on! Try!"

Thord tried. He tried hard, but he found it very difficult. He managed to cut a peat or two but instead of them coming out cleanly and landing on the top of the bank they fell off the tusker into the trench at the bottom of the bank.

"Keep trying," urged father and to his surprise Thord managed to land one or two on the top of the bank. "Very good," said father. More and more of Thord's peats were flying up over the top of the bank and he was beginning to be quite proud of himself. Perhaps he got a little bit too confident.

"Mam," he heard Christane say and then his peat flew off the tusker. He heard a thud and a wail and knew with a sinking feeling that he had thrown the peat a bit too exuberantly. He looked up and sure enough, there was Christane with peat mould in her hair and on her face and mother was comforting her and wiping her face with her sleeve.

"Maybe I'll take over for a bit again," said father quietly and he took the tusker from Thord and began to cut.

The sun climbed higher and the larks, which had been singing a chorus in the sky, became quiet and father said, "Time for a rest." Mother took out the bannocks and butter and cheese and buttermilk and bland in skin bags. Lina said. "About time, too," and piled some cheese on a bannock. Father pushed his hands into his back and stretched himself.

After they had eaten, mother got up and took Christane and Thord with her to look for the little plants which grew among the heather and which she needed to make her Axes-drink. It was still early in the year for much to be growing but mother could find things which no-one else would see.

"We need to get some eccle-girse," said mother. "I don't have much left and I need a lot to help turn the milk sour for making butter." They hunted. Thord was not sure what he was hunting for but he thought he was not quite so big a fool as Christane who kept running to mother shouting "Here's eccle-girse!" when it was a blade of grass or a bit of heather.

Finally mother called to them to come and look at what she had found. Down among the heather they could see some little round pale green leaves.

"Feel them," said mother. Thord touched the leaves. They felt sticky.

"These plants have sticky leaves because they catch insects on them and they get stuck there," said mother. "Later on there will be a blue flower a bit like a violet. These are the leaves I need." Thord and Christane squabbled over who was going to pick them but in the end mother said she would do it herself as they were not very big and she did not want them spoilt. She managed to find quite a few which she said would be enough for just now. They would have to get more later. When they came back to cart the peats home they would find many more then.

Before they went home, father let Thord have another turn with the tusker. This time he was more careful and he was pleased when father said he was doing very well. Next year he would be able to cut a lot more and help father. He was bending over, intent on his work, when he heard another wail.

"What have I done now?" he thought, and then he thought to himself, "Wait a bit. I've done nothing." He looked up to see what had happened to discover that Christane had found a muddy trench to fall in. She must have dived headfirst into it for it was her face that had caught most of the mud. As her eyes were shut it was only her open mouth and little teeth that let you know it was a face.

Mother's sleeve was wielded again and soon a pink face emerged. Her hair was still muddy, though, and would have to wait until mother got some clean water at home.

The sun was sinking lower in the sky as they packed up the cubbie and put it and the tusker and Christane on to Hal's back and began the walk home. It seemed longer to Thord than the way there had been and by the time they reached the house he was very tired. He was glad that his father and mother and Lina seemed tired too. He was a big boy of nine now and it would not do for him to get tired before the others.

Da had the supper ready. He had enjoyed himself he said, cooking for a change. "It's very good of you," said mother. "Not at all," said Da. "You know I would do anything to help you, Ingirid. You know that fine."

Mother busied herself getting dishes for them all and Lina helped her. Da told father that the man from the next house had been round that day with the wooden pin which meant that it was time to think about rounding up the sheep to count them and mark them and roo them.

"He said beulding day would be in three days time and you know you have to go, Magnus, as you're the Lawrightman. Besides you have sheep yourself."

"There was nobody home to pass on the pin," said father.

"He took it to the next house himself when you were not here," said Da.

They sat round the fire eating their supper and hoping that Da would tell them a story, and he did, though they did not realise it when he began. They thought he was just asking questions.

"Did you see the hogboon today?" he asked.

"No," said Thord and Christane. "We didn't see him, Da. Why do you think we would see him?"

"Well, he likes a day in the peat-hill," said Da. "But he really likes it best when you're carting home the peats for then he can play all sorts of tricks. He unties the ropes on the bottom of the peat-caisies and lets the peats roll all over the ground on the road back from the hill. So then you have to stop and fill them up again and it takes time. He pushes folk into the peat banks too, especially when it's wet."

Thord got excited.

"I think maybe we did see him, Da," he said. "Christane got pushed into the bank anyway. She's still got the mud in her hair."

Mother fetched a pail of water and started to wash the mud out of Christane's hair. She was using some soap she had made out of some fat and ashes from the fire as the mud had dried in by now. Christane was wriggling and Ben yelped when some soapy water flew in his eye.

Da was interested in what had happened that day and Thord told him that he had hit Christane with a peat.

"That was maybe the hogboon again," said Da. "It's not likely that you would manage to hit Christane yourself anyway. We'd better make sure that we put out some cream and a bit of bannock for him tonight. Did I tell you about the folk that would not put out cream for the hogboon? No? Well, it was like this . . ."

And soon Da was telling them a long story about some very stupid, mean people who would not leave out cream for the hogboon and all the terrible things that happened to them because of it.

Thord listened carefully. He would need to be sure that they did nothing to annoy the hogboon before the time came to cart the peats home or there would be trouble.

Thursday, 27th May, 1557

Thord woke very early in the morning. He had gone to bed the night before when it was still light outside as he knew that he would have to work hard today. He thought that very likely he and Ben would have to work harder than anyone else.

Early as it was, he could hear that his mother was already up raking out the ashes through the hole in the back. She was trying to persuade Lina to get up and make the bursteen but she was not having much success. Finally after she had fetched some water from the bink and put it in the big pot Lina emerged from her neuk bed yawning and stretching.

"What do we have to get up so early for?" Thord heard her ask.

"It's beulding day," said his mother.

"Oh! Right!" said Lina more cheerfully.

Thord wondered why Lina sounded as if it was going to be a holiday. It was going to be hard work, for Lina too as she had to do some of the rooing.

When they had had something to eat, Thord and his father set out with Ben to round up the sheep on the hill. They would have to work with the other farmers who had sheep on the hill to gather them all together and keep them that way until the counting and the rooing had been done. There was a long day's work ahead of them.

Some of the farmers were already rounding up the sheep and driving them towards the creu. Ben was very good at catching one sheep at a time, like all the other dogs, but rounding them up meant that all the men had to walk over the hill to make sure that none were missed out. If there was one stray one, then Ben would be sent to fetch it. Each farmer walked over the same bit of land as he had done last year and the year before and the year before that so Thord and his father knew where they were supposed to go.

It was a beautiful warm May morning and the lark chorus was busy high in the sky. Thord strode through heather, knocking musty sweet-smelling dust in the air. He saw a few bees winging their way across the heather towards the grass pasture. They would come back to the heather later on when it was in bloom. He wondered if they were the bees from their own hives behind the house. They had a number of tall pointed straw hives there which mother looked after. She needed the honey to layer the butter with and they had some in a big jar also for special treats. And of course the wax made candles for Father Harald and some for themselves at Yule.

There was a sheep with twin lambs to be fetched. It was not often that they got twin lambs and less often that they both lived, but this had been a good year, mild and warm since the lambs were born. They looked fat enough. Thord took Ben and went out round the sheep and drove it towards the rest. He could see that the wool was starting to lift on its back so it was ready for rooing. Maybe it would be easy this year and at least it was warm and dry. If it was raining when the sheep were rooed the fleeces got wet and the sheep were heavy to handle and slippery.

Last year had been bad. It had rained and the sheep were wet and the ground was wet and naturally Thord had got wet. He had tried very hard to catch the sheep for the men to tie their legs ready for rooing. That was his job really, to catch the sheep one by one in the creu and take them out to be tied. But last year had been difficult. He would catch one and it would wriggle and slip out of his hold.

Then he would fall flat on his face and everyone would laugh. But last year he had been eight. This year he was nine and much bigger.

The sun was climbing higher in the sky and it was getting warmer. By the time they had rounded up all of the sheep they were all hot and tired but there was a lot of work to be done still.

Thord's father went with the two other Lawrightmen to look at the marks in the lugs of the sheep to find out whom they belonged to. They marked the lugs of the lambs with the same marks as their mothers so everyone would know who they belonged to and nobody could claim a lamb that was not theirs.

By the time that the marking had been finished, Thord's mother had arrived with Lina and Christane. Lina started gossiping with the other women and Christane went with her to see what was being said. Most of it she would not understand but she liked listening and pretending she was bigger than she was. Thord thought he could understand why Lina was so cheerful this morning. She would have other people to talk to besides the family she lived with.

"Dod!" shouted his father. "It's time to go in the creu and catch some sheep."

Thord groaned. He hoped that he would do better this year but a lot of the other boys were bigger than him and faster. They would make fun of him again.

Olaf was there. He jumped into the creu and grabbed the biggest sheep he could find. He was just wrestling it towards the gateway when it gave a wriggle, turned round and butted Olaf in the stomach.

"Oof!" said Olaf and fell back over. The rest of the boys roared and laughed. Thord cheered up. "If it can do that to Olaf," he thought, "then it doesn't matter so much if it happens to me." He leapt into the creu himself but he chose a smaller sheep to deal with. "There's no use showing off if it lands you in trouble," he thought.

Soon the men were hard at work tying the feet of the sheep. The women looked carefully at the marks in the lugs and made sure that it was a sheep belonging to them before they started to roo. They plucked the long hair from the back first and then you could see the new wool growing under that.

With some of the sheep the wool came away easily and it was bundled up and put aside in a heap. Soon there were little stacks for each farm. But there were some sheep whose wool did not come away so easily and a long time would be spent tugging it carefully out of the new growth. Others had lost some of their fleece already. Thord had seen the wisps of wool among the heather. They would collect as much of that as they could on another fine day.

When they stopped to have something to eat, Thord was glad to rest. He thought he had done very well this year. He had caught a lot of sheep and had only fallen over once or twice. One of the sheep which had got away from him had thudded into Olaf's back and knocked him over again, on his front this time, and trampled him underfoot. Olaf had got up, nothing daunted, and had run after it.

Thord ate his bannock and cheese. He looked to see if Lina was gossiping again and found that she was, only this time it was one of the men she was blethering to. She was making sure that he had enough cheese and bannocks and she fetched him a drink of ale. Thord heard her say that she had made it herself and that it was very good.

"I know it's good," he thought, "because Mam made it. Lina only helped. Why is she telling him she made it?"

It was time to go back in the creu. There were not so very many left to catch.

The lambs were there too of course but they would be let out as soon as all of the sheep were rooed. They were bleating noisily. Suddenly one of them gave a startled yell louder than the rest. Thord looked across to see what had happened to it and was surprised to see Christane hanging onto its neck.

The lamb bolted for the gateway with Christane still hanging on and desperately shouting "Mam! Help!" Thord reached the gateway before the lamb and stopped it in its tracks. He lifted Christane off. Father came rushing up.

"What happened, Dod?" he asked.

"I don't know," said Thord. "Christane was hanging onto the lamb and it tried to run out of the creu but I stopped it."

"What were you doing, Christane?" asked father.

"I was trying to catch a lamb," said Christane. "The boys can do it and so can I, but it wouldn't stay still."

"You'll need to wait until you're a bit bigger, buddo," said father.

Mother and Lina had finished all the sheep belonging to Kirkbuster and they were helping the woman from the next farm. She was older than mother and was getting tired. Soon they had finished hers too and it was time to load up the caisies and carry the wool home. Thord caught Hal and helped to load the caisies. He looked at the wool and wondered how mother and Lina were going to turn all that lot into cloth and blankets. It was a long job, carding, spinning, weaving. A lot of work. Maybe he would get a new tunic!

The sheep and lambs went back to the hill for the summer. The sheep looked happier now that they had their fleeces off and were not so hot. The lambs were confused, wondering what kind of animals these things were until their mothers found them and they realised that they were sheep.

Hal plodded home with Thord plodding behind him. He was tired now but he had done well today. It was quite good being nine. You could do a lot better.

Da was waiting to hear how they had got on. He had made the dinner again and was pleased with himself. Today's dinner was a great treat. They were going to have some of the cock chickens that had hatched out earlier in the year and which they did not want to keep. They kept the hen chickens of course to get more eggs. But the cock chickens made a splendid feast. Thord did not think he had ever tasted anything quite as good. Da's cooking was very good.

It was almost dark when they had finished so Thord knew it must be quite late. Christane had fallen asleep on father's knee and he carried her through to the sallur to bed. Mother tidied up the dishes and put them away to wash tomorrow. She looked at the tub on the bink and realised that there was no water left in it, so she fetched a pail to go out to the well. Thord jumped up and took the pail from her.

"I'll get it," he said and went out through the door and down to the well. He dipped the bucket in and took it back to mother. He was just going to go out for another when mother said, "That will do for tonight. It's getting dark and we can fill it up tomorrow."

"I think I will go to bed," said Thord. "I would like to listen to Da's story but I will likely fall asleep so please, Da, can you keep the story till tomorrow too?"

Da laughed and said he would. "But the best story today is Christane trying to catch the lamb," he said. "I don't have as good a story as that."

Wednesday, 2nd June, 1557

It was the beginning of June. At this time of year the sun hardly bothered to go to bed at all and the light streamed in through the liora into the house till late in the evening and poured in again a few hours later. Thord thought that it did not seem right to him to go to bed when the sun was still high in the sky but sometimes he was so tired that he just fell into bed and the light did not keep him awake.

He was spending some days now out on the rough grazing herding the kye. He drove them out from the byre in the early morning after the milking was done. Today he was to herd them again and it was time he got up. He could hear his mother and Lina in the firehouse. Lina was fetching the pails to go and milk and making plenty of noise about it. She was grumbling as usual.

"I just thought that I could have gone to the hill with the kye today to do the herding," Thord heard her say to his mother. "There's no butter or cheese to be done today."

"We have the wool to wash in the burn," said mother. "I need you to help me with that. Thord can go today again."

"I wonder why she wants to go and herd the kye?" thought Thord. "It's not a thing she usually wants to do. She gets bored looking after them. She says there's nothing to do but look at kye and she sees plenty of them when she's milking them."

He went through to the firehouse, whistling. He had discovered that he could whistle the St Magnus hymn and he liked to hear it. Da thought he was really clever to be able to do that and he liked to hear it too. Thord thought that he would try and whistle it for Father Harald. Maybe Father Harald would teach him all the words then and what they meant. They were in a strange language.

Lina was still grumpy after she had finished the milking and she splashed her bursteen into her bowl so hard that a lump flew out and landed on Ben's nose.

"Yelp!" said Ben as the hot bursteen hit his nose but after he had waved his nose about a bit the bursteen cooled and he licked it off happily.

Thord took Ben with him when he set off for the hill with the kye. Ben would enjoy a day snuffling about looking for rabbits and mice and running after a heather root if he flung one hard enough. The kye plodded ahead of them, glad to be out in the early sunshine. Thord drove them out past the ploughed fields and out through the hill-dyke.

As they walked on the sun climbed higher, the larks climbed higher and the sunlight and lark-song fell mixed in a soft shower round them. Thord's little caisie with his midday meal in it thumped in a reassuring way on his back. He whistled.

When they reached the hill pasture he could see someone else there already. It was the servant man from the next farm with the kye from there. Thord thought it was strange that he should be in the same place, as the kye from the next farm were usually much farther over on the hill but he was glad to see him. It would be nice to have some company for a change. As long as he had not brought the bull with him. He looked carefully. No, there was no sign of the bull. That was good.

"Hello," he shouted as he got nearer. "It's a fine day."

"Good day indeed," said Einar. "I see you have Kirkbuster's kye out today. Is Lina not with them then? Is she busy?"

"Yes," said Thord. "She's helping my mother to wash the wool. It's a good day for it."

"Oh," said Einar, "I thought maybe she would be here today."

"Oho!" thought Thord. "Now I see why Lina wanted to come here. It's a good job it was me that came. Like as not Lina would have forgotten to count the kye and left some up in the hill, she would be that busy blethering to Einar."

Ben started barking at Einar's kye. He was used to their own ones but these were strange and he thought he should give them a bark. The kye did not like it much. Some turned and ran but the cows with calves ran towards Ben and tried to butt him with their heads. Ben yelped again and ran off for a bit but he soon turned round and began to bark again.

"What did you take that dog up here for?" Einar complained. "A dog in the hill with kye is just a pest."

"He's fine with our ones," said Thord huffily. "Usually it's just our own ones here."

"I'd better take mine away then," said Einar and turned to drive them off. Before he could do that one of his cows butted Ben again and he let out another loud yelp. "Ben's not having a good day after all," thought Thord, but when Einar's kye had disappeared over the brae Ben settled down for a rabbit-hunt and his day improved.

Thord plucked a strong blade of grass, put it between his thumbs and blew on it. A shrill whistle echoed over the hill and startled the shalders who hurtled them selves into the air screeching. Thord tried different blades to see if he could make different sounds. Some were shrill whistles and a few made rather rude noises. The cattle paid no attention to him but munched on steadily.

He whistled the St Magnus hymn again but soon found that he was whistling it faster and faster till it sounded like music to dance to. So he danced. It was a bit strange as when they danced it was usually in a big circle with each one's arms touching the next. But he did his best to dance by himself as if he was in a circle.

"It's a pity that Ben can't dance", he thought. "But maybe he thinks he's dancing with the rabbits."

When the sun was quite high in the sky he ate his bannocks and butter and cheese. One of the bannocks had butter with honey in it which was good. Mother had put bland in the skin bag for him to drink, as she knew he liked it best. Ben had a bit of bannock and cheese too but not a bit with honey on it.

After he had eaten, Thord thought that he would look for some plants for mother to put in her Axes-drink. He could carry them home in the caisie. He liked the bigger sort of plants best, he thought, and he picked a big bunch of tall white things. He was sure that mother would be pleased with them. The day wore on and the sun began to sink in the sky. It was time to go home again. He whistled to Ben. As he walked home he thought to himself that a day herding the kye was fun when it was as good a day as today. When it rained though it could be miserable. "It would be good," he thought, "if we had a big pen out on the hill for the kye and then we could put them there in the morning and fetch them in the evening. That would be a lot better."

When he got home he told his father about his good idea and his father laughed.

"That would be really funny," said father, "if the hill was covered with dykes to keep the kye in! Anyway, there would be nothing for you to do then!"

Mother looked at his plants.

"Oh, Dod," she said. "I can't use these! I would poison everybody! This is cow parsley. You must have seen that the kye won't eat them."

"Oh, well, yes," said Thord. "I did wonder why they had left them. I thought maybe they were just full up."

"Where have you been today, Peerie Dod?" asked Da.

"I've been herding the kye, Da," said Thord.

"Herdie-boy, hmm?" said Da and his face looked sad. "A fine job. Somebody has to do it."

"Why do you look so sad, Da?"

"Oh," said Da with a sigh. "I'm remembering another herdie-boy and what happened to him."

"Tell us that story, Da, please," said Thord. "What happened to him?"

"Something terrible. You don't want to hear it."

"Tell him, Da," said father. "He will need to know sometime. Tell him now. I remember it myself. I was just his age. Tell him. Christane is away in bed asleep, so tell him now."

Thord was worried. It all sounded so serious.

"All right," said Da. "I will tell him, though I don't want to remember it myself. It happened about thirty years ago but I remember it as if it was yesterday.

"At that time the tacksman in Orkney was William Sinclair. He was not a very good landlord and some of his kin thought that he was trying to get rid of our Udal laws and make us become the same as Scotland where the King is supposed to have all the land and you have to give him rent for it.

"There were two Sinclair brothers, James and Edward, who got rid of him out of Orkney. They captured him and killed some of his men and threw him out. William went to his cousin Earl John in Caithness and complained to him. John said he would help and he gathered together a lot of men to invade Orkney and kill James and Edward. But we had heard that John was going to do this so the Orkneymen were ready. James and Edward sent for men to come and help them and of course we agreed to go. We did not want William back.

"I went to Kirkwall to be with them. I left your grandmother and your father behind. Your father wanted to come with me. He was big enough, he said, for he was nine. Well, I know you think that you are big enough at nine to do anything, but I thought he should stay and look after his mother, so he did stay.

"When I got to Kirkwall I found a lot of my friends there and there were many men coming from the North Isles and from Shapinsay. We went to Edward Sinclair to find out what was happening. He was glad to see us all and told us he was waiting for the beacons on the Ward hills to be set alight and when that happened he would know that Earl John's fleet had left Caithness.

"A day or so later we saw the beacon on Wideford hill and we knew that John was coming. Edward thought that he would land at Scapa and we waited in Kirkwall with him. But then a boat came in to Scapa and we were told that John was heading for Orphir. Edward rode off over the hill to join James and told us to follow as quickly as we could.

"We followed. As we went on through Orphir we saw a man running towards us, shouting that John had made for Summerdale and James's men were fighting him there. We would need to attack them from this side. When we drew near, we saw that it was Sigurd and that he was angry and upset about something and as we hurried towards the fighting we asked him what had happened.

"'I don't want to think about it,' he said. 'It is so dreadful. When John landed on the shore he met an old wise-woman and he asked her to tell him who would win the battle. She looked hard at him for a long time and then she said, "Which spills the foremost foeman's life, that party conquers in the strife." And then she turned away and left him. John looked at his men and asked them if anyone of them could solve this riddle for him. "I can," said one of his men. "If we kill an Orkneyman first, then we will win."

"'As they walked on they saw a herdie-boy standing with his cattle on a bit of land. And like the cowards they are, they did not wait to kill a man who could fight back. They killed the herdie-boy.' We could see the tears in Sigurd's eyes. Orkney folk in general are very fond of bairns and do not like to see them ill-treated. This killing would not be forgotten for many a long day.

"We asked Sigurd whose bairn it was. 'That's the strange thing,' he said. 'Those cowards killed him for an Orkneyman but he was a Caithness boy. His father left him here to be a herdie-boy and earn his own keep.' 'That means then that they have killed one of their own,' I said. 'Do they know that?'

"'Oh, they know,' said Sigurd. 'Some of them want to give up the fight now and go back home but of course Earl John will not give in.'

"We reached the scene of the battle. If we had been angry at William before, we were doubly angry now because of the herdie-boy. None of us thought of anything but of trying to kill as many of those Caithnessmen as we could.

"It was a dull day. The cloud was low down and it was raining a bit so that it made it difficult to see what was happening in the battle. We saw Edward Sinclair fighting hard and we ran towards him and joined him. He was swinging his axe and cutting through the Caithness men like a huik through bere in hairst."

"Da," said Thord. "Did you kill any of the Caithnessmen? You, I mean. You, yourself?"

"I did," said Da. "I don't like to think about it now but I did it at the time and it seemed right."

"Did any of them try to kill you?"

"They did, but I was lucky. I was wounded in my left arm but I could still use my axe and I did."

"Is that the axe that father has now?" asked Thord.

"It is indeed, Dod," said Da, "but I don't think he will need to use it to kill anyone."

"What happened then? Did you win the fight?"

"Well a strange thing happened," said Da. "Suddenly there was a break in the cloud and the sun shone through. Not just in a single beam but you know the way it can shine in several places in patches. One of these patches was brighter than the others and it caught the steam rising from the men as they fought. We heard someone shout, 'Look! Look! St Magnus is here to help us,' and indeed we seemed to see the shape of the saint in the light. It was wonderful. We knew then that we would win. We heard Edward shouting. 'Come on, men,' he yelled, 'St Magnus is with us. St Magnus looks after his own. We've won! We've won!' And indeed it was not long after that that the Caithnessmen turned and fled. We chased them and many of them were killed before they could reach their boats."

"Was John killed?" asked Thord.

"Yes. They killed him," said Da and he looked sad.

"I would like to be in a battle," said Thord. "It would be exciting."

"No, you would not," said Da. "It is not exciting but horrible. I hope you never have to fight such a battle but I think it's not likely that you will have to. Things are more settled now."

"James and Edward Sinclair are still alive, are they not?" said father.

"Edward is still alive and well," said Da, "but James is dead. I heard it said that he had killed himself. I don't think he was like his brother, Edward. He was too greedy. He tricked the king of Scotland into giving him a fine estate in Orkney, so it is said. When the king found out he sent him a letter, telling him to explain what he had done. But it drove James mad and he ran out of the house and threw himself over a high craig. The way it was told me was that the evil spirit led him by the oxter into the sea and drowned him."

"Now, Dod," said mother. "You're going to have a bit of bannock and butter - maybe with honey - and then to bed with you. That was a long story from Da tonight and a sad one, but you need to know the things that have happened here in Orkney. It would not do if these men were forgotten and the herdie-boy should never be forgotten. He was doing no harm to anyone. He was just doing a job which has to be done and doing it well."

Thord went to bed thinking of all that he had heard and wondering if he would be frightened to be a herdie-boy all by himself on the hill now. He did not think so for Da had said that he would not likely have to fight and Da knew everything.

Thursday, 10th June, 1557 – Johnsmas

Thord swung his legs over the side of the bed and stood up. It was time to get up. He could hear Lina clattering away in the firehouse and singing a strange song to herself. "Funny," thought Thord. "Lina is very cheerful this morning." He pulled on his tunic and ran barefoot through to the firehouse. He had discarded his rivlins some weeks ago.

His mother was busy at the fire as usual and he heard Da say something to Lina about seeing her young man that evening. Thord wondered where Lina was going to see a young man and then he remembered. It was Johnsmas; Midsummer's Day. There would be a big bonfire in the evening and everybody would be there. It was exciting.

Before the excitement though, the day's work had to be done and Thord was soon on his way to the hill pasture with the kye. He was herdie-boy again and he did not suppose that the kye knew that it was Johnsmas. He whistled as he went and Ben ran beside him most of the way. He darted off now and again when he thought there was a promise of a rabbit but he had no luck. Either the rabbits had seen him coming or they were still fast asleep.

There was no sign of Einar when Thord reached the hill pasture with the kye. "He must be well over on the other side," thought Thord. "Maybe just as well if he has his bull with him." The kye spread out enjoying the grass they could find and the soft new shoots of heather. Thord whistled and the larks echoed him far in the blue sky. It was a warm fine day and Thord thought that it would be a splendid evening for the bonfire. He ate his midday bannocks thinking of the feast to come.

This was the day when the sun hardly set at all. It dipped below the horizon for a little but it left its light in the sky and shone red in a line along the east. The bonfire was to celebrate the light and the warmth and the promise of the hairst to come. Everybody enjoyed it as the heavy work of the Voar was finished and there was a break before the first of the hairst work.

Thord wondered where Einar could be. He was missing him a little. He could spend a long day herding by himself and not be lonely. There was so much to look at and so many things he could do. But today it would have been nice to talk to someone about the bonfire in the evening and the fine time they were going to have. For once the sun seemed to take a long time to climb through the sky.

He decided after a while when the sun had swung towards the west that the kye had probably had enough to eat He whistled to Ben and began the drive

homewards. The kye seemed a bit surprised and were reluctant to go but after what seemed like an age to Thord they began to plod their way towards Kirkbuster. Thord munched on the last bannock as he went.

He reached home to find everyone busy. His mother was making some special bannocks with the last of last year's honey. The bees were busy again by now and the weather had been mild and dry so there should be a good crop of honey this year. Da was helping mother. He was stirring something in the big pot. Lina was helping his father to saddle Hal with the two big peat-caisies. One of them would be filled with some of last year's peats for the fire and some bones that had been kept especially for this.

The other caisie would hold the food and drink that mother thought they would need. Each year they always seemed to need enough food for about twelve people although there were only six of them. Da was going to come too and father was putting a saddle on the mare for him. Da liked to ride the mare in the summer sometimes for she was quiet and would not jump about like Hal did if he got a chance.

"Why do we take so much food, Mam?" asked Thord. "We'll never eat all of that, not even with Christane with us."

"Well, we need to have a bit extra, just in case somebody has forgotten to take theirs," said mother calmly.

"What your mother means, Dod," said Da, "is that some people don't have enough food at this time of year to spare any for a bonfire feast, so your mother takes extra for those people. So that they have something. Like Karl and his mother."

Thord drove the kye into the byre for the night and Lina hurried in with a pail to do the milking. Instead of grumbling away as usual, she was singing her strange song. There did not seem to be very many words to it. La la la was about all that Thord could make out. Still, it made a nice change from complaints.

When they were all ready to go, Da came out and looked round him.

"It's a fine night," he said. "I don't think we'll get cold."

"You'll never be cold with the bonfire, Da," said Thord. "You can sit next it."

"Well, I don't think I'll sit that close, Peerie Dod," said Da. "It might not be safe."

"Why wouldn't it be safe, Da?" asked Christane.

"You wait and see," said Da. "When those young lads start jumping through the flames, it's better to stay clear."

"What would they do that for?" said Christane.

"Just to show off, I expect," said father.

"Ah, well," said mother, "I remember a time . . ."

"Shoosh!" said father.

"What time? When?" said Christane.

Nobody answered her. Mother smiled a little smile to herself and Thord thought to himself, "I bet she means that faither used to jump through the fire. I wonder why? Faither doesn't need to show off. He is what he is and that's that."

"Come on! Hurry up!" said Lina. Thord thought that it was a very strange day altogether. No complaints from Lina and she was actually wanting to hurry up and do something.

It was a warm, fine evening as they walked towards the place where the bonfire would be lit. The sun was flooding gold along the land and the grass in the meadowland, growing higher every day, rippled in waves of rose and gold. From many sides they could hear the 'Krek krek' of corncrakes but they tried in vain to catch sight of one of them.

They could see that the bonfire had already been lighted as they drew near. Smoke was billowing in the sky and there were crowds of people laughing and shouting. The noise swelled over the heather and sent the shalders screeching away as usual. They could hear music too and Thord saw a ring of dancers with arms linked stepping in time to the music and singing and making their way around the fire.

Lina disappeared. Mother did not seem to be worried about this so Thord thought it must be all right though it added to the strangeness of the day. He found Olaf and they wandered off together to watch the dancing and help the other boys to fling extra peats on the fire.

He saw mother and Christane handing round bannocks and cheese and filling up horn cups with ale. He thought it strange also to see Christane handing over food until he noticed that for every bit she offered to people, she ate a bit herself.

"Come and watch the fiddlers," said Olaf, running over to a bank of earth at one side where two men sat, holding the two-stringed gues by the neck, balancing them on their knees. The fingers on their left hands flew over one of the strings, and when they drew their bows across it, the other string vibrated and droned in harmony. The tune seemed to get faster and faster and the dancers' feet flew over the ground. At last the two fiddlers stopped on a final chord and mopped their brows.

"I want to be a fiddler when I am older," said Olaf. "I need to learn now, though, so I've asked faither to make me a gue. He says he'll have to ask Eyvind how to make it for he doesn't know. But he probably does know. He knows everything."

"Can he play one too?" asked Thord.

"Well, I don't know about that. But maybe Eyvind will teach me."

Eyvind had heard him. "You get the gue," he said, "and then we'll see."

More dancers joined the circle round the fire. To let the fiddlers have a rest they started to sing and to move with the singing. Thord saw his father and mother join in. He wondered where Christane was and then he saw that she was with Da. He suddenly realised that he was hungry. He nudged Olaf to see if he wanted to come and have some food, but Olaf was talking eagerly to Eyvind. Eyvind was showing him his gue and telling him what to do with it. He let Olaf try it and he drew the bow across the strings. There was a dreadful wail.

"Ow, Olaf," said Thord. "That sounded just like you've stood on the cat."

Olaf frowned at him and tried again. It was not much better.

"I think he's got a lot to learn," thought Thord, and went off in search of food.

Not far from the bonfire there stood a huge stone. It stood upright, pointing a finger at the sky and in the middle of it there was a hole. It was called the Odin Stone and he knew that Father Harald disapproved of it for some reason. When Thord had eaten, he wandered over to the stone as he could see a few people standing there and he thought there might be something interesting going on. It was there he found Lina, and Einar too. They were standing, one on each side of the stone, with their hands clasped in the hole in the middle.

Da and Christane were standing there too, watching them.

"What is Lina doing now?" asked Thord.

"Well," said Da. "She's promising to marry Einar when they have saved enough to get a place of their own. Maybe in a year or two."

"What is Einar wanting to marry Lina for?" asked Thord in astonishment. "Can't he get anybody else?"

"Oh, I think he likes Lina," said Da.

Thord thought that that was perhaps the strangest thing in all this strange day. He watched as Lina and Einar finished making their promise and then another two came and put their hands through the Odin stone.

"Why is it called the Odin Stone, Da?" Thord asked.

"Odin was one of the gods in the old days," said Da. "And you see, Dod, people still think that there is a strong magic in this stone. So they come here to make their promises and think maybe that Odin will help them."

"Father Harald doesn't like it," said Thord.

"No, I don't suppose he does," said Da.

Da came back to the bonfire with Christane and found a rock to sit on. There were more dancers joining in now. Thord watched them carefully.

"Da," he said. "Is this like the dancing you were telling us about last night? You know. When the seals throw off their skins and dance on Boray Isle? That happens tonight too, doesn't it?"

"Yes, that's tonight," said Da. "Lots of strange things happen on Midsummer's night."

Mother came over and took Christane to join in the dance. Christane got very excited and jumped about all over the place. Her feet did not seem to be following the music. Thord thought he could do better so he joined father and watched what he did carefully. Four steps to one side, four to the other. One forward and one back. Olaf joined in at the other side. In his usual enthusiastic way, Olaf managed to trip over a tuft of grass and fall flat on his face. He dragged the two dancers on either side of him down with him and they nearly fell.

"If you play as well as you dance, Olaf," shouted Eyvind, "then your gue won't last long." Everybody laughed. Olaf did not care. He got up and jumped about as eagerly as ever.

The dancing stopped for a while. Soon Thord knew why Da had not wanted to sit close to the fire. Some of the young men ran towards the fire and leapt through the flames. By this time the flames had died down but it was still a dangerous thing to do. He saw Einar leap over the fire, right over the middle. He sailed over easily and Lina clapped her hands in delight.

His father and some of the older men fetched the bones that had been kept for this evening and took them over to the fire. Thord watched as they said some special words and then threw the bones into the middle of the fire.

"What are they saying, Da?" he asked.

"They are just saying that they are throwing the bones in to make sure that the hairst is good and that everyone will have plenty to eat in the coming winter," said Da.

"Will it work?"

"Oh, it might. Stranger things have happened," said Da.

The sun was beginning its climb again when they went home. Da rode on the mare with Christane and father and mother and Thord walked behind. They left Lina still enjoying herself with many of the other young men and women. The bonfire still burned with a clear light.

Thord tumbled into bed beside an already sleeping Christane. His last thought as he fell asleep was that Lina would be very tired the next day – that same day really – and she would most likely be back to grumbling again.

Sunday, 4th July, 1557 – St Martin o Balymas Day

Thord went through to the firehouse as soon as he wakened to see if breakfast was ready. He found everyone there except Christane who was still asleep. Da was eating his bursteen and shaking his head. Father had finished his breakfast it seemed and was standing at the door looking out. Mother and Lina were arguing. At least Lina was arguing and mother was trying to reason with her.

"But it's a Saint's Day," said Lina. "We always have a holiday on a Saint's Day, or a feast or something."

"Yes, I know it's a Saint's Day," said mother patiently, "but this is July and there is a lot of work to be done and we have never bothered about this Saint's Day."

"Well, why not?" said Lina in a loud voice. "I'm sure this Saint is as good as any other one."

"I expect he is," said mother, "but we don't keep all of the Saints' Days and this is one we don't bother with. All we do with this one is ..."

"We shouldn't make any difference between them," interrupted Lina. "If he's a saint, he's a saint and we should have a holiday."

"But, Lina, I've told you," repeated mother, "there is a lot of work to be done this month and we don't bother about . . ."

"Well, we should," said Lina.

Da stopped shaking his head and said to Lina, "What you are really wanting is a day off work so that you can go and see your young man. But what if he doesn't have a day off? What will you do then?"

"He is getting the day off," said Lina.

"Aha!" said Da, "I thought so."

"Oh, Lina," said mother. "You can go and see him after you've been to Mass. You just had to ask me! All this nonsense about Saints' Days! Tell him to come and have his dinner with us."

Lina looked pleased and stopped grumbling.

"What Saint's Day is this, Mam?" asked Thord, but it was Da who answered him.

"It's St Martin's Day," he said. "St Martin o Balymas and it's a good job it's a fine day."

"Why?"

"Because whatever the weather is like today, that's the weather we're going to have for the next six weeks."

"Are we going to have six weeks of good weather then?" said Thord, looking at the sunlight pouring through the liora and dancing on the specks of dust and smoke rising up.

"That we are," said Da. "You will have good weather for your trip to Kirkwall and you won't get seasick!"

"I don't get sick in a boat," said Thord. "Well, not on the loch anyway." He had never been in a boat anywhere else.

"Well, that's good," said father from the doorway. "After Mass, we're going fishing."

"Great!" said Thord. "Do we have to bother with Mass?"

"Yes," said father in a voice that Thord knew not to argue with.

Da came with them to Father Harald's kirk. The mare walked sure-footed along the messigate carrying Da and Christane who had managed to hitch a lift as usual.

Father Harald was delighted to see Da.

"I thought I might see you today," he said. "It's a fine day for St Martin, isn't it?"

"There," said Lina. "I knew it was a proper Saint's Day." Mother shook her head.

Einar was there that day also. After the service he and Lina walked away together, promising to return to Kirkbuster for dinner.

"It might be a good dinner, too, Dod," said father. "It will depend on what we catch today."

When they reached home they fetched the lines that father and Da and Lina had spent so much time making over the winter. Father tied on the hooks that he had made out of bone. He fastened them on the long lines here and there and tied bits of feather on each one. Then they carried the lines and a caisie down to the shore of the loch where the boat was. Thord could remember father building it out of wood that had come from Norway. All of the boards had been measured and marked in Norway so that it was easy to put together. It had come from a place called Os, which Thord thought was a funny name.

He helped his father to pull the boat down into the water and waded out with it until it almost floated. Then they pushed it off with the oars. He sat down on a thaft and watched how his father handled the oars. His turn would come later but first his father would row out to the best place to catch trout and then they would let out the lines.

The loch was calm and flat and the hills were reflected in the water turning it brown and green. The reflections shivered and broke as the oars dipped and rose and Thord wondered if he looked hard enough, down through the water, he might get a glimpse of Nuckelavee. Then he thought that he would not bother, as he really did not want to see the monster. "Let him sleep," he thought.

The boat was well out on the loch when father stopped, shipped his oars and told Thord to get the lines ready. They had been laid separately in the bottom of the boat and Thord lifted one and gave it to his father. He took the other one himself and began to let the hooks into the water slowly and carefully.

Almost at once there was a tug on his line and he hauled it in. On a hook was a fine big trout. Thord was pleased that he had caught the first one. Then father beat him by catching two on his line. Thord let his line out again.

"I think we're going to be lucky today," said father. "We could have gone fishing yesterday but it is always best to wait until Martin o Balymas Day to make sure if the weather is going to be with you or not. And it is a fine day today."

It did not take them very long to catch a large number of trout and at length father thought they would have enough to deal with for one day.

"We can come another day and catch some more," he said. "I think this will be plenty for now."

Thord rowed ashore and they filled the caisie with trout. Father thought they should just leave the lines in the boat for next time so they tucked them under a thaft and laid a stone on top of them to stop them blowing away if the wind rose. They carried the caisie home between them. It was not so very far to go.

Mother was pleased to see so many fish. She took some of them to cook for dinner and looked for some large dochan leaves to roll round them so that she could set them at the edge of the fire to bake. She would put some oatmeal round them, she said.

Father set to work to gut the rest of the fish and wash them in the burn. Then he fetched a wooden barrel and he and Thord put layers of fish and layers of salt between them into the barrel.

"Right," said father when they had finished. "Now we can leave that for a bit. We need to take them to Kettil as soon as we can so that he can smoke them for us. I hope he has found enough hard wood round the shore to do that. When we get them back they can go into the skeo to dry."

The skeo stood near the house but separate from it. It was built of stone with gaps left between them so that the wind could blow through it and dry the fish. Sometimes they kept cheese and butter and reestid mutton there too.

They were just turning to go back into the house when they heard a screech from Christane. Father started to run, thinking she must have been hurt, but she came running out of the door of the house, the cat in front of her trailing a small fish by the tail.

"Look!" she cried, tears running down her face. "The cat's taken my own special peerie fishie. Mam was just going to bake it for me."

"Never mind, buddo," said father. "Dod and I will get you another. Don't cry."

Back they went to the barrel of fish and hunted for a little one. Thord thought there was one near the top and he found it quite quickly. Father spread the salt again more evenly and Thord took the little fish down to the burn to wash the salt off. He went back to the house with it and gave it to Christane.

"Make sure the cat is out this time," he said. Christane pulled a face at him.

"Say thank you to faither and Dod for finding that fishie for you," said mother.

"Thank you," said Christane. She watched mother roll it up in a dochan leaf and set it near the fire.

"When will it be ready?" she asked.

"It won't be long," said mother, "but why don't you go and play outside until it is ready. It's such a fine day."

Thord and Christane went down to the burn. There were lots of yellow flags, or segs, growing in a clump beside the burn and Thord pulled some long leaves. He twisted them and pushed the points through the broadest part of the leaves. When this was pulled through a little way it made a fair keel for a boat and soon the burn was awash with little green seggie-boats on their way down to the loch. The water was cool and fresh over Thord's feet and he could see that the hem of Christane's dress was getting wet.

They made two big ones and set them off together, one for Christane and one for Thord. It was a race and Thord's boat was just edging ahead when he heard the splash.

"I knew it," he thought as he turned round, and sure enough Christane was lying on her tummy in the water. He helped her up and took a soggy Christane back to mother.

Mother was just coming out of the house to say that the dinner was ready.

"I don't know how many times she's fallen in the burn this year," said mother. "What were you doing down there?"

"Sailing seggie-boats."

"Oh, well. Did yours win?"

"I don't know. It was winning, but then Christane yelled so I don't know."

Lina and Einar arrived and Lina made a fuss of Christane and dried her and put another dress on her. Thord stared. Usually Lina grumbled if she had to dry Christane off. Maybe Einar had some kind of magic about him that made Lina different. Whatever it was, it was good.

And the dinner was very good. "Fresh trout baked with oatmeal must be the best thing to eat ever," thought Thord. "Specially when you've caught it yourself."

Mother had cooked some peas as well to eat with the trout and Da asked for a second helping of those. There was just enough. He said he would tell a really good story in return for getting extra peas, so when they had all finished eating they reminded him. And again Thord thought that he had forgotten the story for he began with a question.

"Have you seen the man in the moon?" he asked. Thord said he had.

"Do you know that there are two men in the moon and that they are Orkneymen?" said Da.

Thord and Christane stared at him.

"It's true," said Da, "and this is how it happened."

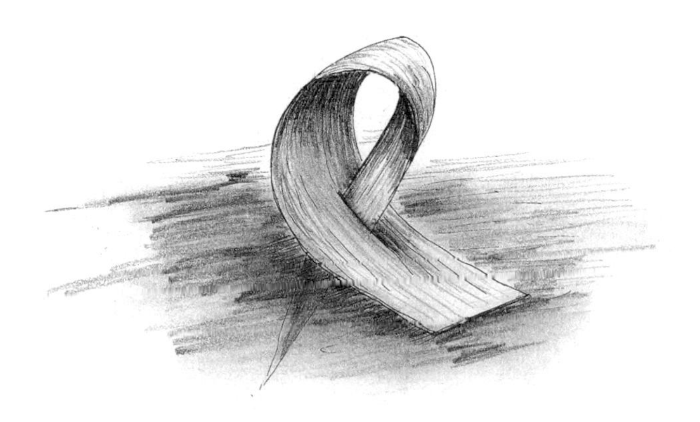

"A long time ago there was a huge ship. It was called the Mester Ship because it was so huge. It could be loading wood in Norway at one end and the other end would be in Stronsay loading peats. It was so high that the tops of the masts used to bang against the stars when it sailed.

"Well, one day it was sailing along when the wind rose. All the sails were set and the ship was going as fast as fast could be, when the captain saw that they were heading straight for the moon and the top of the mainmast was going to bang into it.

"He tried to turn the boat round and he nearly managed it but she heeled over and the top of the mast banged into the moon in spite of all he could do. Well, there were two Orkneymen up in the crow's nest and when the mast banged against the moon, they got flung out and thrown onto the moon and they are still there for the Mester Ship never got back to fetch them off."

Thord could see father smiling at this story and he found it funny himself.

"Tell us more," he begged.

"Another night," said Da. "It's time for bed now. No, no, Christane, there's no point in going outside to look for the men in the moon. You'll have to wait for a week or two. The old moon is nearly done just now."

Friday, 23rd July, 1557

There had been a drying wind for some days now and when Thord woke he heard his father say that today would be a good day to start cutting the hay in the meadow. The grasses had grown tall and thick there since the kye had been going out to the hill pasture. Once they had cut the hay and dried it and gathered it in and the grass had grown a little again, then the kye could go back on the meadow. In the fine days over the winter they could go out there too and enjoy a bit of daylight for a change. It was dark in the byre in the winter. There was no liora to let in light and let out smoke.

After breakfast they set off for the meadowland, all of them. Da had decided that his cough was so much better that he would come too, riding on Hal, and perhaps he might manage to do a little cutting. Father had asked for some help from some of their neighbours and Thord was pleased to see Karl and his mother had come. He ran across to Karl with Ben at his heels.

"Is this your dog?" asked Karl.

"Well," said Thord, "he's really faither's dog but he comes with me a lot. We're good friends."

"He's nice," said Karl. "Can I speak to him?"

"Yes. Go on," said Thord.

Karl knelt down and patted Ben. Ben licked his face. Karl thought that was funny.

"Want a bit of bannock?" asked Thord, offering Karl a bit with butter and cheese on it which he had not finished at breakfast.

"Thanks," said Karl.

Da arrived on Hal's back and he had a caisie with the huiks in it for cutting the hay. Father took them and handed them round to Lina and mother and Karl's mother and the rest of the neighbours. There were two left so he took one himself and told Thord to take the other.

"Come over here and I'll show you and Karl how to cut," he said. "Then you can take it in turns to cut some."

"Look," said father. "This will be the best way for you. Pull the hay this way with your left hand and then cut it towards you. See, this way, Dod."

Thord watched his father for a little and then tried himself. At first he could not get the huik to cut. His father showed him again.

"Keep the stalks tight," he said, and then Thord began to realise that he could do it.

"Don't take too much to start with," said father. "Just take a little. You can take more when you can manage it."

Thord took another handful, thinking carefully about it, his tongue sticking out of the corner of his mouth. This time his handful came away cleanly and he laid it down behind him and took another handful. Karl was watching him closely and Thord thought that he might be able to do it too when his turn came. He worked forward as hard as he could, looking straight ahead at the grass in front of him.

When he had done a lot, as he thought, he stopped and looked around. Dismayed, he realised that everyone else was far ahead of him, not just a step or two as he had thought. There was a flat calm sea of hay on the field except for a little stream of waving grass right in front of him.

"Let me try now," said Karl. Thord handed him the huik. Karl tried. He was no

better than Thord had been to begin with, but Thord told him what his father had said and soon Karl could manage to cut too.

"We're away behind," said Karl. "Maybe you should cut so that we can catch up."

"Oh, I think you can do it fine," said Thord. "It won't matter about catching up. Faither must have seen that we're way behind and he'll come back if he thinks we should catch up." Karl smiled happily and cut away manfully for some time.

Thord saw Da coming towards them on Hal and shouted to him to come and see what they had done.

"That's very good," said Da as he slid down off Hal's back. "Maybe I can have a turn now. Just a short one."

Karl gave Da the huik and they watched as he swung it back and through the hay with a big stroke. The grasses fell over his arm and he laid them down behind them. Thord's jaw dropped.

"Da," he said. "You've just cut more in one go than I can do in ten." Da laughed.

"I've had more practice," he said, "and I expect you're doing it a different way. You need a lot of practice to do it this way, so don't try it until you're a bit older." And he swung the huik again and another great armful fell to the ground.

Da cut for a little and then Thord tried again. He thought he was doing it much better but he did want to cut as much as Da in one go.

"I'll have a try at it," he thought and swung his arm back and through the grass like Da. Nothing happened. The grasses bent and sprang away from him and slid along his arm. He heard Da laughing behind him and after a little Karl joined in too.

"Hmmph!" said Thord. "What did I do wrong?"

"You have the huik turned the wrong way, Peerie Dod," said Da. "Turn the cutting edge up a little."

Thord tried again and this time he cut some of the grass. Some stalks were left standing and he slashed at them again. More fell.

"Good," said Da. "Try again, Dod." Thord tried again. Still more fell this time.

"That's it," said Da. "Keep at it. Watch the edge of the huik."

With each stroke Thord got better though he could not match the easy way that Da had done it. Still he felt quite pleased with himself. He swung away until his arm ached.

"I think you should give Karl a try," said Da. "He will want to learn too."

Thord handed over the huik a little reluctantly, but if the truth were known he was glad to have a rest.

Karl's first tries were as bad as Thord's had been, if not worse, but with Da's encouragement he finally managed to do it and his face lit up when he felled his first armful. When they got to the end of their pathway, they found that everyone else had moved on to the next field. Thord and Karl hurried to catch up with the rest but Da said that he thought he would go home now with Hal. He said he felt a bit tired and Thord was worried that they had kept Da too long out in the field helping them.

"No, Dod," said Da, "I enjoyed helping you and Karl. I think I've done a good day's work and Magnus will be surprised to see what you can do, let alone your Mam."

Thord's father was indeed surprised to see what Thord and Karl could do.

"How did you learn that?" he asked.

"Da showed us," said Thord.

"Well, well. You can just do a good row now between you and maybe you can keep up," said father with a twinkle in his eye. They tried very hard to keep up but in the end father had to come and help them to finish off.

As they walked home in the evening father said, "Well, next year I won't need anyone but Karl and Dod, that's for sure."

Karl's face split in a huge grin.

Mother and Lina fetched bannocks and butter and cheese and some of the trout that Thord had caught to make supper for everyone. Karl and his mother came with them along with the rest of the neighbours. Plates were filled and Lina poured ale for the men and some of the women. Thord and Karl had bland. Thord looked round for Christane, expecting to see her stuffing herself as usual, but he could not see her anywhere.

"Where is Christane, Mam?" he asked.

"Faither has her with him," said Mam.

"I don't have her," said father. "I thought you were taking her home."

"Oh, my mercy," said mother. "Where is she?"

Father and their neighbour Eyvind ran back out to the field hunting everywhere as they went. Thord could hear them calling to each other as the rest waited anxiously at the house. Suddenly they heard a great shout from Eyvind.

"Here she is, Magnus. Over here."

Father came home carrying a very sleepy Christane. Eyvind had found her sound asleep by the side of the field.

"She was running through the hay all day," said mother. "We had to watch out as she would come rushing out of the bit we were cutting shouting 'Boo!' every now and then. 'I'm a trow,' she said. I just thought she had gone to you, Magnus, when she disappeared."

"I think she's ready for her bed," said father.

"I want something to eat," said Christane and everybody, including Thord, laughed.

When they had finished eating father put Christane to bed and she fell asleep straight away. Thord was going to ask Da for a story. He was tired but he was too excited about learning to cut with a huik and doing it, as he thought, so well, that he knew he would not sleep for a long time.

But Da was asking Eyvind something.

"Have you got your gue with you?" said Da.

"I have that," said Eyvind. "I thought maybe you would like a tune."

"Hear that?" said Karl. "Eyvind's going to play. Maybe Mam will sing. She sings fine."

Karl's mother sang them a long ballad about the three sisters and Eyvind played the gue while she sang. It was a sad story, Thord thought, but a good one. Nearly as good as a story from Da. And Da seemed to be really enjoying it all.

"Oh, there's nothing like the old songs," said Da when Karl's mother had finished. "Come on, Magnus! It's your turn now."

Thord stared in astonishment as his father sang with Eyvind playing again. This time it was a song about a king in a glass castle which seemed a bit strange too but it was interesting and a good story. Thord had heard his father sing before but just little tunes and he thought that this was really a very odd evening. It would just need his mother to sing now, something more than a baby song, and he would feel he was dreaming.

Then it was his mother's turn. Thord shook his head to see if he would wake up. His mother sang about a king going hunting in the green wood. The story did not seem so good to Thord but the tune was very fine.

Da was enjoying himself. It was not often that he was entertained. It was usually Da who was entertaining everyone else.

Sitting round the fire and listening to Eyvind play was making Thord very sleepy. And Karl too. Karl had almost fallen over once or twice.

Mother came across and whispered to Thord.

"I think that this will go on for quite a while. Da is enjoying himself and so is your father. You and Karl had better get to bed now. Karl can sleep beside you. Christane is in our bed."

"Can he really, Mam?" said Thord. "That will be great. Come on Karl. We'll go to bed now." Thord pulled the sleepy Karl with him to the sallur and they tumbled into bed. Karl was asleep before Thord pulled the cover over him.

Thord himself fell asleep with Eyvind's merry music floating through his dreams.

Thursday, 29th July, 1557

"Dod! Dod! Wake up!" said father, shaking him.

Thord opened his eyes reluctantly and looked at his father.

"What is it, faither?" he asked.

"Come on. Get up," said father. "We're carrying home the peats today. We need to get started as soon as we can. There's a lot to do."

Thord swung his feet over the side of the bed and stood up. The weather had been so warm and dry for the last few days that he had had no need of his tunic and his skin was beginning to get brown. They had all spent most of the time in the hay field, turning it over and over to dry and then building it into coles, small heaps ready for carrying into the yard.

They had been very lucky with the weather this year. Some years in the hay time it rained a lot and then father had to hang the hay over ropes to dry and it took a long time. And sometimes it would not dry at all and the hay would rot. In those years there was very little to feed to the kye in the winter so they would have to eat straw and the bare grass that they could find on the fields inside the hill-dyke.

Today there was not a cloud in the sky. It would be a good day to carry home the peats.

Thord had gone to the peat-banks a few times with father and Lina since they had cut the peats. They had turned them over and back to make sure that they dried and now they were quite hard. They would carry them home and then stack them at the end of the house as they did each year. There were some peats left from last year and they could build the stack on top of them.

"Come on, Dod," said father. "We need to get Hal and the mare saddled and the peat caisies put on them." He disappeared out of the door as he spoke and Thord ran after him. He followed his father into the stable and led Hal out while his father fetched the mare. They hung the large peat caisies on each side of the saddles. Hal did his usual little dance to show that he was pleased to be doing some work.

Father swung another caisie onto his back. It had a rope that fitted over his shoulders and lay across his chest. Mother and Lina and Christane came out of the door carrying bannocks and cheese and some skin bags. Thord hoped there was bland in the skin bags. Mother fetched two other caisies like the one father was carrying and she and Lina hoisted them onto their backs and they all set off for the peat-hill.

Long before they reached the peat banks, Lina was shading her eyes and looking eagerly to see if Einar was anywhere in sight.

"If she keeps looking at the distance like that all the time," thought Thord, "she'll trip over the long grass or something."

Just as this thought crossed his mind, he saw Lina stumble and fall flat on her face. The bannocks and cheese shot out of the caisie and into the grass.

Mother rushed over to Lina and asked her what had happened. She began picking up the bannocks and bits of bannock and the cheese.

"Thank goodness Mam had the bland in her caisie," thought Thord.

When they reached the banks Lina was delighted to see that Einar was there, busily filling caisies for the farm where he worked. Lina dumped her caisie down with a thud on the ground and ran over to speak to Einar.

"I bet that bang on the ground has battered a few more bannocks," thought Thord.

Father was looking carefully at the ropes tying the bottoms of the peat caisies. Instead of having a lid on the top of them, the peat caisies had a lid on the bottom so that they could empty them quickly when they got home.

"Well," said father, "they seem to be tied tight enough. I've checked them all so if they let go when we are on the road home, then we'll know that it's the hogboon. I hope somebody remembered to put out some bannocks and cream for him last night."

"I did, faither," said Thord. "Da told me to do it, so I did."

"We should be all right then," said father. He began throwing peats into the caisies and mother and Thord helped. They could hear Lina giggling away at the next bank and father was just going to shout to her to come and do her share when mother said, "Leave her. She'll be more willing to do her share if we leave her for a little." Sure enough, before they had finished filling two of the caisies Lina came back and started work, filling the caisies as if her life depended on it. Father stared but mother just smiled.

When they had filled the caisies on the horses, mother emptied the bags of bland out of her caisie and filled it with peats too. Father helped her to swing it onto her back. Thord helped to swing a full caisie onto father's back and they set off for Kirkbuster. They left Lina to look after Christane until they got back for a second load. Thord led Hal, anxiously checking the ropes on the bottoms of the caisies in case the hogboon managed to loosen them in spite of having bannocks and cream. Father led the mare and mother walked behind with her load.

When they reached home, they found that Da had tidied up the peat stack and was waiting to help them unload. Thord thought that mother looked very tired after carrying the caisie such a long distance. Da thought so too, but mother said she was fine and that Lina would carry the next load home in any case.

"I see that the hogboon has been happy with his bannocks and cream," said Da, loosening the ropes and letting the peats fall onto the ground. They did not need to worry about how they fell as the inside of the stack was just a heap of peats anyway. It was only the outside that had to be carefully built so that it was rain-proof.

"I'll tidy these up a bit before you get back with the next load," said Da.

"Don't go and do too much," said father. "Dod and I can do it later."

Mother was sitting resting on the low dyke beside the brig-stones. She was quite ready for the walk back, she said, and Lina would come home with the next load.

Hal frisked around a bit again after getting rid of his load but the mare just turned and plodded calmly back the way she had come. The sun was hot on Thord's back as he walked back to the peat-banks. He was glad he had not bothered with his tunic. There was a little breeze, as there almost always is in Orkney, and Thord was grateful for it as it cooled his back a little.

They got back to the bank to find Lina looking a bit down in the dumps. Einar had taken a load home, she said, but he was coming back. Lina and Christane had been looking for plants for mother and they had found a lot of eccle-girse. Mother was very pleased. They had found eyebright too which was good.

Christane thought it must be time for some food and mother agreed so they ate the bannocks and cheese. Nobody seemed to worry about them being broken and battered. They tasted just the same after all.

Father checked the ropes again and the caisies were loaded once more. This time mother stayed behind with Christane to hunt for more plants. Lina grumbled as she hoisted up her caisie. Einar was still not back and she saw no sign of him as they went carefully towards Kirkbuster. Either the hogboon was in a good mood or father's knot tying had been extra careful, but they reached home without a mishap once more. Da had tidied up and was waiting for them again. They emptied the caisies.

"Right! Off we go again," said father. Thord's legs were beginning to wonder how often they would have to go to and fro leading Hal. Hal did not frisk around this time either. With father leading they plodded back again.

It was on the last run home that the hogboon decided that he had not perhaps been given enough cream. Father had checked the knots as usual, carefully. Mother and Lina had filled their caisies and hoisted them up on their backs. Father was just going to fill his when Christane climbed into it and pretended to fall asleep.

"Maybe she is asleep," thought Thord, peering at her.

Father laughed and swung her onto his back instead of peats and they all set off together down the hill again.

Halfway home the hogboon played his trick. The rope on the caisie that Hal was carrying on his left side let go and the peats tumbled out and down around Hal's feet. Hal snorted and jumped and the weight of the caisie on the other side made his saddle slip round. He was too tired to bolt and Thord was pleased about that as he thought that he himself was too tired to pull him back if he did bolt.

They stopped. Caisies were swung down for a little and everyone except the sleeping Christane helped to put the peats back in again. Thord thought that he had seen his father's lips move but he did not hear him say anything. He held Hal's head and stroked him. Hal gave him a nudge. The mare stood quietly, swishing her tail to chase the flies away.

They moved on again and it seemed the hogboon had given up for they reached home and Da without anything else happening.

Da had made supper. He had eaten his and promised them a story while they ate theirs. And, of course, at the word supper Christane had woken up and was looking for her share.

"We'll have to carry home the rest another day," said father, "and it won't be tomorrow as we have to take the coles of hay into the yard and build them into skroos. Einar is coming to help and maybe Eyvind. If it's weather. But with the sunset tonight I think it will be fine. And St Martin o Balymas Day was fine after all. We have been lucky this year."

There was a lot of work to be done over the next few days, thought Thord. They had to finish carrying home the peats and then build the outside of the peat-stack properly to hold out the rain. They had to get all the hay into the yard and make sure that the skroos would run water, as father called it. They would get some help, of course, but they would have to give help in return, which meant more work.

"I wonder if we will get it all done in time," thought Thord. "In time for our trip to Kirkwall. It will be terrible if we have to stay here and finish the work and not go after all."

Father must have been watching Thord's face.

"Don't worry, Dod," he said. "We'll get it all done in plenty of time."

Thord smiled happily. If father was saying that, then it must be true.

At night he dreamed of the cathedral in Kirkwall. He had no idea what it would look like but thought it must be like Father Harald's little kirk only much bigger and in his dreams, that is what it looked like. The windows were so high up that he thought they must reach all the way up to heaven and maybe God could peep in through them.

Tuesday, 10th August, 1557

Thord stood beside his father on the beach in the morning. At their feet were the caisies they were taking to Kirkwall, filled with wadmell, cloth which mother had woven on the loom in the sallur, and with pen-feathers from the hens and geese. They could trade these at the fair and buy some wood for a new plough and some handles for implements. The wood came from Norway. The boat they had on the loch had been built from wood from Norway. The wood had come to Orkney shaped and marked and they had put it together themselves.

Father Harald had shown him some pictures in a book, which had some trees in them. They seemed to be much bigger than the boor-trees that grew at the back of the house. He told him that the trees in Norway grew very tall and straight. Many people wanted them because they made good masts for boats. Thord wondered if the mast of the Mester-Ship had come from Norway. It seemed likely.

The sea was washing gently into the beach at Skibbigeo, where they stood. Thord watched the men getting the boat ready for the journey to Kirkwall and loading some cargo. One of them went over to the well and filled two skin bags with clear water to drink on their journey. Then they hoisted the mast into place and hauled up the sail. There were two pairs of oars for the boat was a fowerern. The men would row as well as use the sail.

Thord and his father had left Kirkbuster the day before, in the evening, and had walked the two miles or so to Kettil's house to stay with him until they could get a boat to Kirkwall. Father had warned Thord that they might have to wait for some time as it would depend on the weather and the tide whether the boat would go or not. It was a long trip but if the tide were with them, they could make good time.

Kettil thought they might be lucky.

"The tide is right for going to Kirkwall," he said. "If you go in the morning, you will catch the flood most of the way and that will carry you into Kirkwall quickly.

Maybe you can get there by the afternoon. If there is not too much wind."

St Martin's good weather held and this morning there was bright sun and just a little breeze. Kettil had come with them to Skibbigeo and he helped them to climb aboard when Sweyn and his sons had made the boat ready. Sweyn pushed off from the shore and Kettil waved as they rowed out to the open water. Thord sat on a thaft in the bow and watched the sunlight sparkle on the water as they turned towards the east.

There was just enough breeze to tug at the sail. Sweyn asked father if he would take a turn at the oars and sat in the stern himself, grasping the steering oar. The tide towed them onwards and the boat slid past the cliffs and geos, heading for Eynhallow Sound.

The sun was climbing higher when they came beneath Costa Head and saw the sea sliding rapidly through narrow channels on either side of Eynhallow. Although there was hardly any wind, they could see the racing water breaking here and there as if in a storm.

"Is it always like this here?" Thord asked his father.

"Well, we should ask Sweyn," said father. "He will know best."

"It depends on the tide," said Sweyn. "It looks rough just now because this is the strongest part of the flood tide. It will calm down later and then of course it starts coming back out. And it gets just as bad the other way. We can go this way now only because the tide is with us. If it had been an ebb tide we would have to wait until it had passed."

"How do you know where to go?" asked Thord, staring at the swirling water.

"See there," said Sweyn. He pointed to a house standing on a long, low ness away before them. "That's Aikerness," he said. "You must get the house in line with the cairn on top of Gairsay and that shows you the channel."

With that he headed the boat starboard and the tide rushed it forward. Thord found it exciting to be travelling at such a speed. The land seemed to rush past. He watched the terns folding their wings and diving straight into the waves. They bobbed up again with tiny fish in their beaks, tossing them and swallowing them.

Sweyn was speaking. He was telling them that Eynhallow was an enchanted island. It had been won back from the sea. A fisherman had gone there with a bright metal knife which he stuck in the earth. The island had stayed above the waves since then. Curls of smoke rose from some houses on the west of Eynhallow and they saw some men in the fields. They waved to them.

"That's Rousay," said Sweyn, "and behind it is Egilsay where St Magnus was killed." They sailed on past Guerness and Sweyn pointed out the round tower of the broch.

"Look over there," said Sweyn. "That's Wyre, that flat island. You can see what's left of Cubbie Roo's castle there."

Thord looked to where Sweyn was pointing and saw a square tower set on a height. "Who was Cubbie Roo?" he asked.

"Some say he was a giant," said Sweyn. "You see these skerries here? Well, he's supposed to have made them. He was stepping across from the Mainland to Wyre with a load of stones and the bottom fell out of his cubbie and the stones fell here and made the skerries."

Thord was not sure whether to believe Sweyn. He thought he might tell as good a story as Da, perhaps.

The sun shone with a strong light over the islands and Thord could see a pattern of little fields full of ripening crop. Farther to the east a tall tower pointed an accusing finger at the sky.

"What is that?" Thord asked Sweyn, "that tall thing over there?"

"That's St Magnus's kirk on Egilsay," said Sweyn. "They say it was built on the spot where he died." So it seemed, thought Thord, that St Magnus had two kirks. The one in Egilsay looked really big. Was the one in Kirkwall bigger?

"We have to go into Tingwall," said Sweyn. "We have some fish to land here." He swung the boat in towards a sturdy stone pier and waved to the man standing there. Thord was glad to be able to get off for a short time and stretch his legs. The ground seemed to be going up and down a bit, though, which felt strange.

Sweyn off-loaded the fish and spoke to the man on the pier. He asked him if he was going in to Kirkwall to St Olaf's Fair but it seemed he was not.

They got on board again for the last part of the journey. Gairsay lay ahead, where Sweyn Asleifson had lived long ago. Part of his house could still be seen as the boat slid past the Taing. There was a building on the Taing, a barn with a kiln, just like the one at home.

"Look, Dod," said father. "Look over there."

Thord peered into the distance, trying to make out what father was pointing at. He could see a hill rising at one side, steeply. There was land at the other side too but in between there was a dip and silhouetted against the skyline he saw a tiny square building.

"That's the cathedral, Dod," said father.

"But it's so small," said Thord.

Father laughed. "We're miles away from it yet," he said. "Wait and see. It will get bigger and bigger as we get nearer."

As they sailed on the cathedral did indeed seem to grow slowly larger and larger. The sun was sliding over towards the west and the tide had stopped flowing in towards Kirkwall. It would be an hour or so before it began its rush back out; time enough to get into Kirkwall with slack water.

They drew slowly nearer. Some houses began to be seen and Thord thought he could make out another kirk nearer the shore. A long flat strip of land extended to the right of a line of houses along the shore and Thord could see a boat sailing round the end of it into what looked to him like a loch.

Sweyn steered the boat towards the narrow strip of land, the ayre, and took it carefully round the end into the Peerie Sea. The cathedral soared above them, shining rose-red in the noon sun and Thord could find no words to say. It was not like his dream, at all. It was so much better. His eyes rose to look at the square tower on the top. He heard Sweyn say that Bishop Reid had looked after the cathedral well. He had repaired it and built on to it and it was now splendid.

In front of the cathedral there was another large building, with strong, thick walls.

"That's the castle," said Sweyn.

"Who lives there?" asked Thord, finding his voice at last.

"Well," said Sweyn, "at the moment it's a Frenchman. His name's Bonot and he was sent here a while ago by the queen to look after the castle and collect the taxes. But, of course, Edward Sinclair of Strom is sometimes there too. He's the Lawman. Sheriff they call it now."

"There's another big castle over there, beside the cathedral," said Thord.

"That's the Bishop's Palace," said Sweyn. "Bishop Reid has repaired that too, and he built that round tower on the end, see? He lives there when he's in Orkney, but just now he's away to France, I think."

Thord looked round him at the huge buildings and the spread of houses. His eyes wandered over the glittering expanse of the Peerie Sea. At the far end of it he could see what looked like another kirk. That meant that there were three kirks here; the cathedral, the kirk near the shore and this one, which looked very fine. It had splendid glass windows. Thord could see the sunlight glinting off them.

"There's another kirk, faither," he said. Father looked round at it.

"I remember being in that one," he said. "It's the chapel of St Duthac. The windows are coloured, with pictures in them you can see when the light shines in. It is something to see, but not as good as St Magnus."

"What is the other kirk?" asked Thord.

"St Olaf's," answered Sweyn. "Bishop Reid has repaired that too."

"He must be a great man," said Thord, "and clever, if he can do all this building."

Sweyn and his father laughed. "He gets other men to do the work, Dod," said father, "but he is the one who tells them to do it."

Sweyn took the boat into a pier beside the castle and Thord and his father collected their caisies and stepped ashore.

"We want to stay until Saturday," said Father. "Will you be back here by then to take us home again?"

"Oh, yes," said Sweyn. "I am staying in Kirkwall for most of the fair. I'm supposed to take some goods to Gairsay tomorrow but I will be back after that. I'll see you in the town I expect."

"That's fine," said father. "Now, Dod, we'd better go and find your aunt's house first. We can come back and see the cathedral after."

"Where does aunt Freda stay?"

"In the Laverock. This way." Father turned to the right and they hoisted their caisies onto their backs and set off, past the castle and the cathedral and the Bishop's Palace.

Thord listened to the sounds all round him. It was all so different to the quiet of Kirkbuster. There you heard the birdsong, the occasional moo from a cow or bleat from a sheep, the shush of the waves on the loch shore, the rustle of the wind in the grass. Here there was clatter and bustle. People were milling around in front of the cathedral and some were setting up stalls for tomorrow. A horse went trotting by pulling a cart, something Thord had never seen.

And there were the voices; so many voices. Hardly any were speaking Norn. Thord was learning to speak Scots with Father Harald and he thought that his father could speak it quite well. Da, he thought, could understand Scots but he pretended not to and he would not speak it. His head began to spin with the noise and he hoped that they could find aunt Freda's house soon.

Father stopped to ask someone which house Adam Flett lived in and they were directed to a house farther up the narrow street. Father knocked on the door, which Thord thought very strange. It was opened and they found themselves looking at a young girl with a white apron over her dress. They heard a voice from behind her call, in Scots, "Who is it, Minna?" Father shouted back, "It's Magnus and Thord, Freda. We got here fairly quickly. The tide was with us most of the way."

Aunt Freda came hurrying through from the back of the house and hugged them both. "Look at the size of him," she said, in the Norn. "I haven't seen him since he was a baby, and I've never seen Christane at all. How is she?"

"She's fine," said father. "She wanted to come but she's too small yet. We have to find her a wooden horsie."

Aunt Freda laughed. "That should be easy enough," she said. "Now come in and have something to eat and you can put your caisies in your room. Adam will be back soon. He'll be pleased to see you both."

Thord thought aunt Freda's house must be as good as the Bishop's Palace. There were two big rooms at the front of the house and another room and kitchen at the back. There were stairs going up to more rooms and he and his father climbed up behind aunt Freda and she took them into a room with a big bed covered with a patchwork quilt. It looked very grand.

"Fancy sleeping up in the roof!" thought Thord as he dug in his caisie to find the butter and cheese that mother had sent to aunt Freda.

They went back to see the cathedral when they had eaten and Thord stood in awe and looked at the vast space in front of them as they entered. The roof seemed as far away as the sky and the pillars soared over them. As he looked down the length of the building he could see an enormous round window. He followed his father in silence as he went towards the shrines of St Magnus and St Rognvald.

Thord remembered the procession on St Magnus Day and he could not quite believe that he, Dod, now stood beside the bones of the saint himself. He wished he could remember all the words of the hymn that Father Harald sang. What were they?

"Nobilis, humilis, Magne martir stabilis."

That was part of it.

"O quam felix cernitur, Hinc Orchadia."

They went out blinking into the bright sun and father turned to go down towards the bridge and the oldest part of the town. They walked along the narrow street that led to the bridge. Under the bridge ran a noisy burn, channelling its way down to the Peerie Sea. The water in the burn did not seem to be clear and sparkling. It looked a strange muddy colour. Thord was puzzling over this when his father said, "This is the Papdale burn. The women use it for their washing further up from here. That way, see?" Father pointed up to the right.

They crossed the bridge and the road swung to the left. They saw the kirk of St Olaf on their right and they could see the sea glinting at the end of the street. They walked down to the shore.

"Look, Dod," said father. "That's the way we came this morning. Past those islands. It's a long way. You can't see the whole way we came from here. You can see as far as Gairsay and Rousay."

There were more boats here, hauled up on the shore. Houses stretched along the shore to each side of them. Thord thought Kirkwall was a very big place.

"Better go back now and see if Adam is home," said father. "And you had better get to bed early tonight. There will be a lot to see and do tomorrow. And we have to find a peerie wooden horsie."

Wednesday, 11th August, 1557

Thord woke to the sound of someone hammering on the door and shouting, "Adam! Adam! Come quick!" He ran over to the window and looked out. A man was standing at the door, looking up. He shouted again, "Adam!"

Father woke up and came across to the window.

"What is going on?" he said. They heard Adam open his window and say to the man in the street, "What is it?"

"There's an English fleet here in the bay. Thirteen ships and their boats are coming ashore now. Hurry, man. Come and help. We'll need all we can get."

"Has someone been sent up to light the beacon on Wideford Hill?" asked Adam.

"Yes. We've sent Andrew and Torval. It will be lit soon but it will take some time for men to reach us. We've sent for Edward Sinclair. He is the only one who can save us but he is at Strom and it will take until tomorrow before he can get here. We need all we can get right now."

"I'll be right there. Just need my clothes and my axe," said Adam. There were more men hurrying up the street, shouting and knocking on doors. Thord had never heard such a noise before, such an uproar.

Father was tying on his rivlins. He turned to Thord and said, "Dod, I want you to stay here with Freda and look after her. She may have to leave the house and go out into the country, so you will go with her if she has to."

"Are you going with Adam?" said Thord fearfully. "Don't go, faither. Don't go. Da said that fighting was not good. Don't go!"

"I must go," said father. "Even if I had been at home at Kirkbuster, I would have had to go when I saw the beacons. But I am here so I can help now."

As his father went out of the door, Thord heard him shouting to Adam, asking if he had another axe. He watched from the window as they went out of the door into the street, axes in hand.

"What if anything happens to faither?" he thought. "How will Da and me look after Mam and Christane?" He felt tears come to his eyes and start trickling slowly down his cheeks. "Oh, Da was right," he thought. "This is not exciting. This is horrible."

His aunt Freda came into the room and stood beside him. She put an arm round his shoulders and hugged him. "Don't worry," she said. "Adam and Magnus are strong and careful. They will be all right."

"Will we have to leave?"

"Not right away. We'll wait until we hear what is happening. We need to know what these Englishmen want."

They waited for a long time and nothing seemed to happen. They could hear some shouts far away in the distance but they saw no-one at all. Aunt Freda went to the door and looked out into the street but there was still no sign.

"Come, Dod," she said. "Let's go to the end of the street and see if the beacon is lit yet."

They walked past the lines of houses and at the end they looked towards the west. The beacon was alight and the red glow shone fiercely on the top of the hill.

"The other beacons will be alight by now as well," said aunt Freda. "Come. We had better get back into the house."

Still for a time they heard nothing but distant shouting. Suddenly the sound got louder and they could hear screams as well as shouts. When they looked out, they saw smoke rising from beyond the cathedral, towards the shore. Soon they heard yells and the sound of feet running. A man came rushing past them shouting, "They're setting fire to the houses!" Women and children came hurrying past, heading for the fields beyond the town.

"Do you think we should go with them?" asked Thord.

"No. Not yet," said Freda. "We will wait for news of Adam and Magnus."

Thord thought that this was the longest day he could ever remember. He waited and waited, listening all the time to the distant uproar. Aunt Freda tried to get him to eat something but he was not hungry. The day crawled slowly by with no news. The smoke drifted over the town in the light wind but there were no more shouts of fire and no other streams of people running to the fields. Thord thought that waiting for news was as terrible as the fighting itself. What was happening? Where were father and Adam?

As the sun began to sink in a red and angry sky, the distant sounds lessened. Just when Thord thought that he could bear it no longer and would have to go and find his father however dangerous it was, he heard footsteps. He peered down the street and saw his father coming towards them, limping a little. He ran to him and said, wide-eyed, " Are you all right, faither? Have they gone away?"

"No," said father. "They have not gone away. Some of them have gone back to their ships but they are just waiting for tomorrow, to start again. But there are many of them in the cathedral. They have captured it and they are going to try to get the castle and the Bishop's Palace tomorrow, we know."

"What have they burnt?" asked Freda.

"All of the houses along the shore, and the ones on the street up to the cathedral. They needed to know, of course, that no-one could hide in those houses and attack them. Now there is nothing between the shore and the cathedral but ashes."

"All those poor people," said Freda. "What will they do."

"They are alive at least," said father. "The English did not manage to kill any of them because they ran off. The houses can be built again."

"Will they burn these houses too?" asked Freda

"Adam doesn't think so," said father, "but he wants you to come with me now, when it is a bit darker, and come into the Bishop's Palace. The Lawrightmen have decided that some of them will keep the castle and some the Palace. Adam is one of the ones in the Palace and he wants you there."

Suddenly Thord was ravenously hungry. "Can I have something to eat, Aunt Freda?" he asked. Freda laughed.

"To think of the times I have asked you today if you wanted something to eat!" she said. "Of course you can. Come and eat something while I pack up as much food as I can carry to take with us."

"I can carry some too," said Thord, "and faither."

Thord emptied the caisies of the wadmell and pen-feathers, and shook his head. All thoughts of the fair had gone from his head all day and only now did he remember. The cloth and feathers should have been sold by now. They should have been looking for the wood they needed. And they should have had a wooden horsie. He took the caisies downstairs for aunt Freda to fill.

"What happened to the fair, faither?" he asked. Father looked grim.

"All the merchants have lost most of their goods, Dod," he said. "The English just took everything. Helped themselves! Maybe some managed to save something. It was early this morning that they came ashore. Maybe some of the merchants had not brought their goods to the fair yet."

When Freda and Minna had finished packing, Thord and his father lifted the caisies onto their backs and they all left the house by the back door. They walked up through the creu and over the fields to the Bishop's Palace. They found Adam there waiting anxiously for them.

"Come inside," he said. "Quickly! There are a good few of them still in the cathedral and I expect they will be watching."

Thord looked over to the cathedral before he went inside. He felt sad to think that enemies were standing beside the bones of St Magnus.

There were a many men inside the Palace and Thord saw women and children there too. "All the families," he thought. "Like us. I suppose we're Adam's family at the moment."

"Oh, fine," said Adam, looking at the caisies. "You've brought food, Freda. I hoped you would. I don't know how long we will have to stay here for safety. It will depend on how long it takes Edward Sinclair to get here. And how many more men we can raise. We are lucky in one way. Since it's St Olaf's Fair there are a lot more men here than usual. It would have been a lot worse today but for that."

"I want to know what happened today," said aunt Freda, " and why Magnus is limping. You haven't told us that," she said to him.

"Oh, that!" said father. "That's nothing." Adam laughed.

"I'll tell you," he said. "When we first went out, we went down towards the shore and saw the English boats landing there. They didn't come through the oyce. They just came straight ashore and hauled up their boats on the beach. There were hundreds of them it seemed – a lot more than there were of us at any rate. We hid in some of the houses and waited for them. We thought if we could catch them in the narrow street we would stand a better chance and for a while it worked.

"We managed to hold them back for a time. None of our men were killed though some were hurt, but we killed some of the English. Then they realised that they couldn't get at us because of the narrow street – so they started to set fire to the houses. And some of them went round behind the houses and we thought we might be trapped in the street. We came back over the bridge and began to make our way up to the cathedral to save it. Some of us walked in front as a lookout and the others followed, looking back the way.

"Your father, Dod, was walking in front when an Englishman burst out of the lane in front of him and stood on his foot. He was a great big fellow with leather shoes on him. Your father only has his rivlins and the man's shoe crunched his foot. You should have heard your father yell! He was really mad. He swung his axe in the air and then you should have heard the Englishman yell! He leapt in the air and shot off down the street with your father and his axe after him."

"Well, I would have caught him too," said father, "but I couldn't run because my foot was so sore. I think he maybe broke some bones."

"Let me see it," said Freda. "I brought some ointments and things with me in case I needed them. Your mother and I learned a lot from our mother, Dod," she said, "and I expect she will teach Christane."

"We help her," said Thord. "We collect plants for her."

"Good for you," said Freda. "Magnus, I think your foot is just badly bruised and swollen. If I put this on it will help."

"What's in that ointment, aunt Freda?" asked Thord.

"Oh, this and that. But there's a little blue flower called self-heal in this. It's very good."

"We've posted some sentries," said Adam, "but I don't think we'll see anything of the enemy until daylight tomorrow. Most of them went back on board the ships. But they'll be back tomorrow, I know. We had better get some sleep. There's plenty of floor-space although there's not enough beds to go round. Freda, I think that the women are using those rooms over there. The men will just be in the hall here I think."

"I brought some blankets," said Freda. "Here, Dod, you take this one."

Thord wrapped the thick blanket round him and lay down beside his father. He wondered what would happen tomorrow. He hoped his father would not need to fight again, but he thought it very likely that he would need to. They would probably all have to fight to get rid of these Englishmen.

"Why are these men here, burning the town and taking the cathedral?" he asked Adam.

"Well, I'm not sure, Dod," said Adam. "Some say that the English Queen Mary has sent them to protect the English fishing fleet on its way home from fishing cod, but if that's so, where is the fishing fleet? I'm fairly sure that sailed back three weeks ago, if the North Isles men are to be believed. So these thirteen ships are not protecting them.

"Others are saying that the Queen sent them especially to invade Orkney and burn the town and loot what they could to punish Bishop Reid for not doing what she wanted him to do."

"But," said Thord, "Bishop Reid is a good man so he should not be punished. And anyway, he's not here."

"Yes, well," said Adam, "I think perhaps it's a punishment for the Orcadians maybe. There has been a lot of trouble from English pirates here for some time. The Scottish government has been complaining to the English about it. Maybe that's what it's all about. Or it may be that some of the English fishermen never find their way home. And that's not always our fault."

"I wish Edward Sinclair was here," said father.

"He'll be here tomorrow," said Adam. "I'm sure of that. Then we'll be fine. We just have to hold out till he gets here. We can manage that."

Thord thought that he would never go to sleep. Too many thoughts were going round and round in his head, some of them uncomfortable ones. What would happen if his father got killed? No, he was not going to think about that. He would think about Edward Sinclair instead and remember what Da had said about him. He wriggled on the hard floor. He knew father was not asleep either.

But so much had happened that day and it was late and he fell asleep still thinking about Da and Edward Sinclair.

Thursday, 12th August, 1557

Thord woke to a bustle in the hall. It was still very early but men were coming and going and women were handing round food and telling the children that there was nothing to worry about.

"It's fun, isn't it?" Thord heard one woman say. "We're staying in Bishop Reid's palace. Isn't this grand?"

Adam had gone out already, to see what was happening and if the English were coming ashore again. Father was still here, wriggling the toes on his left foot and wincing when he touched it.

"Freda is right, Dod," he said to Thord. "There's no bones broken and it is not very swollen. The ointment must have helped a lot."

"What's happening, faither?"

"We don't know yet. There are still men in the cathedral but we haven't heard if the boats have come ashore yet. They will come without a doubt. We have to be ready for them. I wish Edward Sinclair was here."

Aunt Freda came over to them with some bannocks and cheese, cheese that mother had sent with them.

"I don't think mother would ever have guessed that we would be eating her cheese in the Bishop's Palace, faither," said Thord.

"No, I don't suppose so," said father. "I hope she hasn't heard about this battle yet. If she has, she will be very worried."

"She will know by the beacons, faither," said Thord. "She will know that something's wrong."

"Yes, Dod," father sighed. "I suppose so."

Just then some men came back into the palace. People hurried towards them to find out what was happening now.

"The English are coming ashore again in their boats," said one of the men. "We could see them loading some heavy things into them. At least that's what it looked like. One of the men from Weyland came into the town. He had been watching them from there and he thought it was a cannon that they were loading."

The other men looked grim. This was not good news. If they brought cannon ashore it looked as if they were going to stay for some time and reduce the town and the castle and the palace to rubble.

Where, oh where was Edward Sinclair?

There was a flurry of footsteps and two men came running in.

"The English are nearly ashore," said one, "and we think they have cannon with them. It will take them some time to get them off the boats. Should we go and try to stop them?"

"There are still not enough of us here to do that," said another.

Adam came in. He looked tired, as if he had already done a day's work, and maybe so he had.

"There are North Isles boats at Carness," he said. "I went out to see if they were coming and some had arrived. I told them to wait there until most of the boats had arrived and then make their way to Papdale. If they do that, then the English will not know that they are there and they can take them by surprise."

"Which islands had they come from?" asked father.

"There were three Shapinsay boats, two from Rousay, one from Egilsay and one from Wyre. They said the Gairsay boat was just behind them."

"If some of them are there already, then the rest will not be so very long in coming," said another man. "You were right, Adam, to tell them to wait. They will make a good force when they are gathered. Papdale you said?"

"Yes. Thought it was the best place," said Adam. "The East Mainland men will go there in any case. To Carness and Papdale. Some of them will come into Inganess but they will still come through Papdale."

"A lot of the West Mainland men will come to Scapa, I suppose. Better send someone there to direct them."

"And meet Edward Sinclair, I hope," said Adam.

"Then I think we are all agreed that we had better wait for Edward Sinclair and the rest of our men. It would be foolish to do anything today that might cost us any men. We would be better to send messengers between all the groups and see what Edward wants to do," said a man who seemed to Thord to be as old as Da. He wondered if he had fought at Summerdale. If he had, then he would know how horrible it was and would want to make sure that nothing went wrong. Thord heard one of the men call him George and he thought that that was a very strange name.

Adam and the man called George talked together for some time. They decided to send men to Carness and Papdale and to Scapa. Then Adam thought that they should go to the castle and see if they could manage to talk to some of the men there. They could arrange some signals between them, he thought. He and father prepared to go and see what was happening outside and if it was safe to go to the castle.

No-one was paying any heed to Thord. Aunt Freda had disappeared towards the kitchen and father was busy talking to Adam.

"I can sneak out behind them," thought Thord. "Then maybe I can see what these English look like and their cannons, whatever they are."

When Adam and father went towards the door, Thord followed. Nobody stopped him as he went through the door after them and they were deep in talk to each other and did not notice him. They walked round the side of the palace hidden from the cathedral and made their way round some houses towards the castle. Some of the castle was in ruins but the walls had all been built very strong and thick. The part that was left looked stronger even than the Bishop's Palace.

Adam tapped softly on a small door at the back and a voice said, "Who is that?"

"Adam Flett, the Lawrightman," said Adam. They heard the bolts being pushed back and the door opened.

Adam and father were just going in when father turned round and saw Thord following them.

"I thought I told you to stay with Freda," said father angrily. "This is not safe."

"I wanted to be with you," said Thord.

"Get in," said father. And Thord slid through the door. It shut with a clunk behind them.

When Thord looked around, he realised that there were not so many men here as there were at the Bishop's Palace. If there were as many English as he had heard there were, then he thought that it was wise to wait for the rest of their men to arrive before they challenged the enemy. They would be safe inside these great buildings.

"Come up on the roof, Dod," said father. "We can see what is happening easily from there." Adam and father and Thord climbed the winding stone stairs and came out through a little wooden door onto the roof. There was a wall to shelter behind and they went over to stand behind it. From there they could see across the bay and make out the islands lying on the horizon.

Thord gasped. In the bay huge ships lay at anchor, their sails furled. Thord had never seen ships like this. They towered above the water and seemed as if they had castles built on each end of them. Instead of one mast, they seemed to have two or three.

"I wish Da could see this," thought Thord. "They look just like the Mester Ship, I think."

On the beach he could see many smaller boats hauled up and men wrestling with heavy loads. Some of the smaller boats were going back out to the big ships again. "Maybe to fetch more men," thought Thord gloomily. He wondered how even Edward Sinclair could deal with all this. It was frightening.

As they watched, they saw that some of the English had unloaded their boats and were hauling something very heavy up towards the castle. When they were a fair distance away still, they stopped. They could see men putting a round ball into a long pipe-shaped object. One of them had a torch which he lowered onto the end of the pipe. There was a flash of flame, a bang, a screaming noise and then a ghastly thud as the cannon ball hit the wall of the castle.

The castle shuddered. Thord shuddered too and looked white-faced at his father. Father was looking intently out to sea, past the huge ships.

"I think I can see some of the North Isles boats," he said.

"Will the English ships try to stop them?" asked Adam.

"No," said father. "The small boats are too busy taking men ashore and it would be impossible to stop them with the big ships, even if they weighed anchor. They can't do that while they have men ashore in any case."

Another gang of men had hauled a cannon into place. Another ball came whistling through the air and thudded into the castle wall.

"Time to go," said Adam. They went back down the stairs. The men in the castle were placing lookouts on the roof. A system of signals was arranged between them so that they could tell what was happening at each place. The most important signal was the one which told of Edward Sinclair's arrival.

Where, oh where was Edward Sinclair?

When they reached the palace again, they found aunt Freda in a terrible state. She had realised that Thord was missing and was frantically trying to organise a search for him.

"You should have known this would happen," said father in exasperation. "You should have told Freda where you were going."

"I wouldn't have got anywhere if I had done that," said Thord grumpily.

"This isn't a game, Dod," said father quietly.

"I'm sorry, faither. I'm sorry, aunt Freda," said Thord. "I'm sorry for upsetting you both." He thought, "but I'm not sorry I went all the same. I would never have seen all those things if I hadn't."

The day dragged slowly on. A messenger would come now and then with news of the North Isles men, or the East Mainland men, but the news they were waiting for never came.

Where, oh where was Edward Sinclair?

The man called George came and spoke to father. He had fought at Summerdale, he said, and he remembered Da.

"I remember your father fine," he said. "Thord Magnusson. He has the same name as me. We fought together. When this is over and you go home, tell him Thord Rendall was asking for him."

"But they call you George," said Thord.

"So they do, so they do," said George sadly. "That's Kirkwall for you. It's full of Scots and Scots speakers, and they change all the old names because they don't know them. If you say Thord, it sounds like George to them and so they say George. Anyway, my friends call me Dod, so there you are."

"I'm Dod too," said Thord.

As the day wore on there seemed to be a change in the weather. Thord thought he could hear a whine sounding in the light wind and wondered if it was going to rain. Sweyn appeared late in the afternoon with his son.

"We've left the boat in the Peerie Sea," said Sweyn. "We haven't been to Gairsay yet. All those ships in the bay put us off. And now the weather's turning. I think it's going to blow a gale tomorrow, maybe. The sky's showing signs of it. We thought we would come here for safety and to see if we could help a little."

Father was pleased to see them.

"I've been worrying about you," he said. "We'll just have to wait and see what happens now."

It was very late in the evening when they heard the sound they had been waiting for. The clop of a horse's hooves came nearer and someone banged on the door.

"Anyone here?" boomed a voice, and a tall, grey-haired man strode into the palace. "Borrowed a horse from someone at Scapa. Have to make sure he gets it back. Now, how many men have we got here?"

Thord got his first glimpse of Edward Sinclair and he was not disappointed. The hero of Summerdale was now a fairly old man but he was tall and straight as ever, his voice was as loud as ever and only his grey hair suggested that he was not the young warrior who fought with Da. "I wish Da was here," thought Thord, but he wondered if Da would really want to be here. He thought war was terrible. Edward Sinclair on the other hand looked as if he was enjoying himself.

There was another bang and thud from the English cannon, but this time the thud was on the wall of the palace.

"Gracious me," said Edward Sinclair. "Cannon!"

Adam and father looked at one another. Thord could see they were wondering if the English had managed to capture the castle as they had the cathedral. Father went to ask the lookout if there had been a signal, but it seemed that the English had decided to bombard both buildings and try to take them both. Adam gave the lookout instructions to send the signal telling of Edward Sinclair's arrival.

There were a few more bangs and thuds and then silence. Perhaps the English had gone back to their ships for the night or they were inside the cathedral waiting for the morning.

Thord heard Edward Sinclair say to his father, "I knew your father well in the old days. And this is your son, Thord? Named after his grandfather. Just fine. Now, you and Adam had better let me know what arrangements you have made so that we can make our plans for tomorrow."

Thord fell asleep that night listening to Adam and his father and Edward Sinclair discussing their plan of attack for the morning. The wind was no stronger but it still had that odd note in it. "Rain," thought Thord. "It's going to rain." His eyes closed.

Friday, 13th August, 1557

It seemed to Thord that he had only just fallen asleep when he was awakened again by the chatter and bustle in the hall. He could hear Edward Sinclair's booming voice giving orders to the men. The man called George came over to him.

"Well, Dod," he said. "You're awake I see. Come into the kitchen with me and we'll see if we can find some food. Freda's there, I expect."

Thord followed him into the kitchen. Freda and Minna were there with most of the other women. Thord heard them asking one another how much of this or that was left. It seemed they had all taken plenty with them as he heard Freda say, "That's all right then. We have enough for a day or so. Today will tell us how long we have to stay here."

George found some bannocks and cheese and he and Thord sat down on a settle at one side of the kitchen.

"Faither," said Thord.

"Don't worry," said George. "He has had something to eat already and he asked me to look after you. You and I will have to stay here, I'm afraid. I'm too old to fight now and you're too young yet."

"I could fight," said Thord. "If faither has to go and fight, I can fight too."

"Well, well, I expect you could," said George, "but we have something important to do too. We must stay here with a few of the men and make sure that signals and messages get sent properly, to help Edward. When we've finished this we can go up the tower and keep watch. I need a drink of ale, I think. I wonder if Freda has any?"

They went in search of Freda and she said that there was some ale, but not much. More ale was being brewed in a kirn here but it was not ready yet.

"It would give you a sore stomach, George," said Freda, "but you can have this." She handed him a skin bag with some in it. George thanked her and took the bag with him as he and Thord mounted the stairs in the tower. Thord went leaping ahead but George told him to wait as he came puffing up behind him.

"We need to take care. Have a good look out through the windows as we go up. Maybe we can see what's happening."

When they finally reached the top and stepped out a flurry of wind caught them and banged the door behind them.

"Wind's getting up fast," said the man on duty as lookout. "Look over there."

They could see the boats coming ashore from the ships, full of men. Many were already on shore, hauling the cannon into position to start bombarding the castle and the Bishop's Palace again. Men were running out of the cathedral to meet them. It looked to Thord as if there were thousands of the enemy and there was still no sign of the Orkney army.

The wind rose still further and Thord knew that it would be a full gale before long, one of those sudden gales that can come out of nowhere, flattening crops and whipping the sea into a frenzy.

"Look there!" said the lookout, pointing towards Scapa. Thord looked and could see a huge mass of men moving across the fields from Scapa. As he watched, he saw Edward Sinclair and his father stride out to meet them. Adam left with them but he headed cautiously round the east end of the cathedral.

"See," said George. "He's going to Papdale to find the North Isles men and the

East Mainland men. He is going to tell them to wait there until Edward and your father lead the South Isles men and the West Mainland men into the town to confront the English. They will drive them towards Papdale if they can. And then they will be caught between them."

The cannons began to roar again. Thord could see the flash of flame and hear the peculiar whistling noise. Thud went the cannon ball into the wall of the castle. Another flash, nearer at hand and a cannon ball thudded into the wall of the tower beneath them. The wall shook but stood firm.

The wind was rising still. It was blowing from the southwest and along with it blew the cries of men determined to drive back the enemy. Edward Sinclair was leading his army into battle for the second time. Thord shivered as the wind gusted over them.

"Come," said George. "You'd better come down inside again, Dod."

"No," said Thord. "Please, no. I must see faither. I must see where he is."

Suddenly the wind blew the sound of Edward's advancing army into enemy ears. In that same instant the English realised that far from meeting no resistance as they had thought, they would have to fight. They stood in silence for a moment as the wind turned the trees into a heaving, waving sea of green. Then they turned towards the Orcadians with a yell.

Edward's army burst like a wave upon the palace and divided, surging along both sides in a headlong rush. Edward led the left flank forward and Thord could see his father, Magnus, at the head of the right flank. Thord watched, rigid, his hands clenched at his sides, as his father rushed upon the enemy, whirling his axe and yelling at the pitch of his voice. He could see men fall before him as the grass had fallen before Da's huik. Then the enemy broke and ran.

Edward drove all before him at his side. He had taken the enemy by surprise and they ran. Thord was sure that they would only go some way before gathering together again and turning to fight. He wished his father would not run so hard after them. Let others do it. His father ran on.

And now they could hear the yell from the other men at Papdale. They must have seen the English coming and they gave them no chance to regroup. The enemy turned and fled towards the shore. Thord could not see his father any longer. The Orcadians were running after the enemy and he thought his father must be among them.

They could see some boats being pushed out from the shore but the wind was blowing at gale force now and as they watched one of the boats lost its oars, turned broadside onto the waves and turned over. The wind was howling out to sea and more boats turned over. Some managed to reach the ships but they could not take the boats on board and some of the ships were hauling their anchors and trying to steer away from the shore and shipwreck.

Some of the enemy had formed a group and were fighting back. They knew that the boats were gone, most of them sunk, none to return to fetch them. So they fought. Thord could not see what was happening or who was winning. He strained his eyes, hoping for a glimpse of his father. George had his arm round Thord's shoulders and was hugging him tight. His face was strained and white too.

The enemy group became surrounded by Orcadians and they could see that the fighting had stopped. Soon they saw a group of prisoners being marched into the castle. The cannon were seized by laughing groups of Orcadians and hauled up before the cathedral. More prisoners arrived at the castle.

Most of the ships in the bay had hauled anchor by now and were running before the storm. A few boats tossed in the furious waves.

"Flood tide starting to come in again," said George. "That will make the sea worse. The boats don't have much chance."

Another boat overturned as they watched.

At last Thord caught sight of his father. He was limping again and holding his left arm. It was bleeding. Thord gave a cry.

"Faither's hurt," he said and rushed pell-mell down the stairs and out into the hall. He reached the door just as his father came through.

"Faither! Faither!" he yelled. "What's happened to you?"

"A sword blow. It fell on my arm before I could turn away. I don't think it's that deep," said father.

Freda came rushing up with water and strips of cloth. She washed the wound, put some ointment on it and bound it up.

"I don't think it's so very bad," she said. "It should heal quite quickly. Keep the bandage on to protect it for a bit."

"Where is Edward?" asked George.

"At the castle with the prisoners," said father. "He is fine. Not a scratch on him. There is some magic about him I think."

"What are they going to do with the prisoners?" asked George.

"Oh, they are going to ransom them and let them go back to their ships," said father. "That is if this wind lets up and their ships can come back for them!" Father laughed. Then he looked at Thord and said, "What is the matter, Dod? What are you crying for?"

Tears were streaming down Thord's face. He had not meant to cry but he found he could not stop.

"I thought you were killed," he sobbed.

Father hugged him with his right arm.

"No, no, Dod," he said. "I'm fine and so are all the Orcadians. We did not lose a single man."

"What about the enemy?" asked George.

"Yes," said father quietly. "They have lost a great number. Not so many to us. But the wind has been the death of a great many."

A long time later Edward Sinclair strode in, laughing and shouting.

"Well, we gave them what for, eh?" he said. "And all our men are fine. We have found a lot of things they left behind. There's the cannon, of course, but they left money as well and there is the ransom money. There will be enough for everyone to have a small share, I would say. It's all in the castle at the moment along with the prisoners. Sort it all out tomorrow. Tonight we are going to celebrate. Come on ladies and help us."

A huge bonfire had been lit before the cathedral and men were gathering from all round. Thord washed his face to try and get rid of the tear-stains and followed his father and George out to the bonfire. He saw Adam coming back round the east end of the cathedral and ran to meet him.

"We won," said Adam. "But then we would with Edward Sinclair."

Food arrived from every house and Edward Sinclair persuaded some merchants to provide ale and wine from their stores. Someone from Egilsay produced a gue and soon there were a great many ring-dances on every available open space. Thord gaped at the scene. The evening sky was turning red from the flames and his head was reeling with the music and singing and dancing. It was a tremendous sight.

After the grim events of the day, all of them seemed determined to enjoy themselves as much as they could to forget what they had been afraid of and what they had seen. Many of them ate too much and many of them drank too much. Thord had never seen men so drunk before and he could not understand why they were acting as they were. It was very strange.

The last of the gale whirled the sparks from the bonfire high into the air, scattering them like glowing stars above them. Thord gazed at them as he fell asleep beside his father, exhausted from the long, anxious day.

Saturday, 14th August, 1557

When Thord woke up the next morning he could not at first understand where he was. He had been dreaming and the noise of battle was still in his head. Here instead there was the noise of laughter from somewhere beneath him. He looked around carefully and then realised that he was in his bed at aunt Freda's house. He shook his head to clear it and tried to remember how he had got there. He could hear his father and Adam talking to Freda and bursting into laughter now and then.

He wondered how late it was but he thought by the light coming through the window that it could not be so late in the day. He got up and looked through the window into the street. People were coming and going, lots of people. He thought he saw some of the people who had run away into the fields two days – no, it was three days before. He leant out to hear what they were saying.

"No, beuy, better that my house was burnt then that we were all killed. I can build a house again."

"All my goods burnt! How am I going to manage?"

"Hey! Do you know that old William here ran away before they started to burn the houses?"

"Wasn't going to stay and get my beard singed, was I?"

"They are saying that the merchants will give us wood for roofs when we build again."

"Believe that when I see it!"

"No, beuy, it's true!"

Thord went downstairs in search of food. He still could not remember how he had got home last night. He had a vague idea that his father must have carried him. Anyway he did remember that the Orcadians had won the battle and the English had been defeated and driven away. And his father had not been killed. It was a glorious day.

The weather was better, too. The sun was shining again and the wind had died down. It was as if yesterday's storm had never been.

He came into the kitchen to hear Adam telling aunt Freda how he had nearly run into some English as he was trying to get to Papdale.

"I dropped down behind the dyke and lay there for a bit. I was getting worried as I knew I had to get to the men and stop them charging in straight away. As it was I had a job to keep them there until we got the signal from the castle wall. The Wyre men were the worst. They'd brought some ferocious home-brew with them and they were all fired up ready to go. They gave me some. Nearly blew the top of my head off."

"You drove them all towards the shore after that, I gather," said aunt Freda.

"Yes," said father, "but most of the boats had gone and the men had to turn and fight. Some of them surrendered straight away to Edward Sinclair, but others fought on. They did not know what to do as their leader, the admiral, had gone back to his ship and left them."

"What was his name?" asked Freda.

"Sir John Clare, the men said. But I don't think he got far. Someone said his boat overturned out in the bay and he was drowned trying to reach his ship."

"Poor man," said Freda.

Adam and father stared at her.

"Poor man indeed," said Adam. "He was trying to kill all of us."

"He was only doing what the English Queen Mary told him to do. And we know how cruel she is."

"What are they going to do with the hostages?" asked father. Thord hoped that they were not going to kill them. There had been enough killing.

"Edward is trying to get a message to one of their ships to come back for them. He sent one of our merchant ships to signal to them. They are scattered in the North Isles somewhere. If that doesn't work then they will get sent home on one of our ships."

"Where exactly were you fighting?" asked Freda.

"Just where the women do their washing. At the top of the burn where it runs out of the pond," said Adam.

"The burn was running red," said father. "Red as wine. It was bad." He turned to Thord and hugged him. "But today is better."

"Ow," said Thord and winced as father hugged his shoulders.

"What's this?" said Freda. "Let me see, Dod!" She looked at the skin across Thord's shoulders and gave a gasp.

"Where did you get all these bruises, Dod?" she asked.

"I don't know," said Thord, "but maybe it was when the battle was on. George was holding me so tight and my shoulders were aching." Aunt Freda rubbed in some of her special ointment and the ache began to go away.

There was a knock on the door and Adam went to answer it. He came back and said that they had to go to the castle, as Edward Sinclair wanted to share out the goods and money that had been taken. Everyone who was in the battle was to get a share, however small.

"Dod, you can come too," said father, "and then we can go and hunt for Sweyn and see what he thinks of the weather."

They walked down the street to the castle and Thord was surprised to see that some of the merchants had set up their stalls again in front of the cathedral and were trading. Father was pleased to see this and said they would come back later and trade their cloth and feathers for the wood they needed.

"And a peerie horsie, remember," said Thord.

"As if I could forget," said father.

As they went into the castle they heard Edward Sinclair's booming voice long before they saw him. He was sitting at a table with a pile of money in front of him, counting it out carefully and making sure that everyone got something. When he saw Adam and father he signed to them to come over to him.

"Here," he said to them. "These are for you." And he handed them a little bag of coins each. "You both did well. Couldn't have managed without you. Here! Take it!" They thanked him and were turning to go away again when Edward shouted after them.

"Magnus! Come back. I almost forgot. This is for your father, for my friend Dod. For Summerdale. We knew then that we could win and we knew it now. Thank him for me."

Father took the crown and smiled at Edward.

"I'll tell him," he said.

"I'll leave the money with you, Adam," said father later. "Except for Da's crown, of course. And a little for Father Harald for the kirk. There would be very little sense in taking it home as it's here in Kirkwall that I need it anyway. If I need to buy anything, I can just send word to you and you can get it for me."

"Fine by me," said Adam. "I can probably get it to earn you some interest in the meantime." Thord had no idea what Adam was talking about but it was probably something good. Father looked pleased at any rate.

They had spoken to Sweyn and he had said that he thought the sea would go down by the next day, Sunday, and that they could get home by soon after noon if they left early.

"The ebb tide will be with us if we leave early. It will take us straight home again," Sweyn had told them. "I have to go to Gairsay today as I could not get before. It won't take me very long."

"Since they have set up the market again," said aunt Freda, "I think I will go and see what is there, and you will want to go, Magnus, in any case."

"We'll get the caisies and come with you," said father. "Ah. Did anyone remember to take them home from the palace?"

"Minna fetched them this morning," said Freda. "She knew where we left them. They were empty so she carried them both home. I think she's put the wadmell and pen-feathers back in for you." Minna came downstairs carrying the second caisie.

"This is the lighter one," she said. "It's got the feathers in it." She helped Thord put it on.

When they went out into the street Freda turned to Adam and said, "I want you to take me to Papdale and show me where the battle was." Adam protested, saying that he did not think it would be good to take her and Thord there, but Freda insisted. They walked past the market and down the street to the bridge. The wooden bridge was still standing. Thord had thought that the English would have burnt the bridge too and he looked down towards the shore, seeing the blackened ruins of the houses and the scorched walls of St. Olaf's kirk.

"Why did they not burn the bridge?" he asked.

"They needed it," said Adam. "They needed it to get from the shore up the street to the cathedral, over the burn. See! Look where the great wheels of the cannon have left marks on it."

They followed the side of the burn and walked slowly up to the pond at Papdale. The burn was flowing swiftly and the water was clear and sparkling. There was neither red nor milky white in it. As they neared the pond they could see some men hard at work digging in a field beyond the pond.

"What are they doing, faither?" asked Thord.

"They are digging graves for the English who were killed, Dod," said father. "There were a number of them who were killed here. But many, many more were lost in the sea, drowned as they tried to get back to their ships."

Thord was glad to get back to the market in front of the cathedral. He had wanted to see the battlefield and he supposed that he would remember it all his life, but it was a sad place. Maybe it was best forgotten. The hustle and bustle of the stalls soon made him think of other things and he watched while father traded the cloth and feathers and bargained for a new piece of wood for a plough. Thord thought that he got quite a lot of wood in exchange and father said that the feathers were worth a lot as they were always needed for writing, and people seemed to be doing more and more writing for some reason. They made sure that the wood was taken down to Sweyn's boat and went to look for a wooden horse.

Freda had had a fine time going round all the stalls. She had found some spices, she said, which were fine for cooking. She had also found some pottery bowls and had bought some for Thord to take home to his mother.

"Ingirid will like these," she said. "They're a fine size for eating your bursteen. Or mixing things. Or beating eggs."

"Or Axes-drink for Da," said Thord. Freda laughed.

"You are right, Dod," she said. "Axes-drink for Da."

"Have you seen a peerie horsie anywhere?" asked Thord anxiously.

"No, I haven't seen one," said Freda. "I've been round most of the stalls but I haven't seen one."

Thord's heart sank. If they could not find a wooden horse, what would they do? They had to find one. He began to look at all the stalls frantically. There must be one somewhere.

"What are you looking for?" said a voice behind him. Thord turned and saw Sweyn. He smiled at him and said eagerly, "I'm looking for a peerie wooden horsie for my sister. She wants one."

"Wooden horse, eh?" said Sweyn. "I wonder. Let's see if my friend Erland can help us." He led Thord to a small stall at the end of the row.

"Erland," he said. "You don't happen to have a peerie horse, do you?"

Thord looked at the stall. It had lots of wooden things, tubs and cogs, bigger tubs and barrels. Erland winked at Sweyn.

"How would I have a horse here?" he asked. "You can see I only have things made of wood."

"But it's a wooden horsie I need," said Thord, earnestly. "A peerie wooden horsie."

"Well, now," said Erland. "I wonder if this would be any use?" He hunted behind a big barrel and came forward with two little wooden horses, brightly painted. There was a little white and blue one and a bigger red one.

"Oh!" said Thord. He thought he had never seen anything so pretty. "Christane will love that. Where is faither? I need him now to get this."

"He's here," chuckled Sweyn. "Don't worry. He's here."

Father came and looked at the horses. He thought they were very fine and asked Erland where he had got them.

"Did you make them?" he asked.

"No, no," said Erland. "They come from Sweden, these. The merchant from Norway brought them last time. I think he liked them. I think the English did too, for they took them with the rest of my stuff. I found them in the cathedral when they left, hidden behind a pillar."

"Can we have both of them?" asked father.

"Sure," said Erland. Father paid him and thanked him. He took the little horses and smiled.

"Two for Christane!" said Thord. "She'll be right pleased."

"No," said father. "She can have the red one. The peerie one is for you, Dod. For helping me." He gave Thord the white and blue one. Thord beamed.

"Now," said father. "Before we go back to Adam's house, we'll go back into the cathedral. We need to say thanks to St Magnus."

They went up the steps to the great door and walked into the cool dark inside. There were a number of people there already. They passed some coming out and heard one of them say, "St Magnus looks after his own. They made a great mistake when they forced their way in here and took this place."

"Of course," said another. "We knew he would protect us. They stood no chance."

Father and Thord stood by the shrine and thanked St Magnus, each in his own way. Father lit a candle. Thord watched the candle flames flicker in the huge airy building and knew he would remember this day all his life. Whatever happened in the future, this day would stay with him.

"Nobilis, humilis, Magne martir stabilis.

"O quam felix cernitur

"Hinc Orchadia."

Sunday, 15th August, 1557

Thord stood at the pier beside the castle with a caisie on his back and his little white and blue horse in his hand. Christane's red horse was safely packed in his caisie, wrapped in a length of fine cloth which father had bought for mother. He thought she might like to keep it until she needed a special dress for herself sometime. In father's caisie were the bowls that aunt Freda had bought and some of the spices for mother to try. The precious wood which they needed and had come here especially to buy lay at their feet, ready to be loaded.

Sweyn was looking at the weather. It was calm but it was still cloudy and dull. He thought it might rain later but there was no wind to bother them and the sea had gone down since Friday. He thought they would have a good trip home. It was still fairly early in the morning and there would be an hour or so of slack water before the ebb tide set in to carry them out through Burgar Rost and round to Birsay.

Aunt Freda hugged Thord before he stepped on board. She said nothing; just hugged him hard. Adam punched him on the shoulder and said that he and Freda would visit them at Kirkbuster next summer.

"If Sweyn will take us," he said.

"You'll be welcome," said Sweyn, pushing the boat out and hoisting the sail. They waved to one another as they headed for the Oyce and out to the bay. Thord knew that he would never forget his first trip to Kirkwall. Even without the battle it would have been exciting, but the battle was burned deep in his mind and he now knew exactly what Da meant when he said that battle was not exciting; it was terrible. It was strange to think now of that evening when Da told them about Summerdale. He could hear Da's voice telling them about it and how S. Magnus had helped them. He remembered the men in the cathedral saying that St Magnus looked after his own. It seemed he did.

And he remembered Da saying that he hoped that he, Thord, would never have to fight in a battle. He had thought that it would not happen, but it had. Thord was glad, so glad, that the Orcadians had won but he thought it would have been so much better if there had been no fighting. What was the need for it? It was stupid.

They were passing Scargun when Sweyn said that he had to land at Gairsay that day again with some goods. He thought however that he would not go round to the pier at the Millburn but would try and land below the farm called Langskaill. That was the place where Sweyn Asleifsson stayed at one time, he said.

Sweyn took the boat into the shore and the farmer came down to help him unload.

"Come and have some ale with us and a bite to eat, Sweyn" he said.

"No, beuy," said Sweyn. "We can't stop. We have to catch the ebb to get through the Burgar Rost. Thanks all the same."

They pushed off again and headed round the Taing and steered towards Eynhallow.

Thord enjoyed the sail back through the islands. There was Wyre with Cubbie Roo's castle, so much smaller than Kirkwall castle. That was where the men came from who gave Adam the strong ale. There was Rousay with its high hills. And now they steered left and caught the strong flow of the ebb tide. It carried them swiftly past the Evie shore and under Costa Head. Then the headlong rush eased and Sweyn's sons took the oars again and they sailed for home.

Kettil met them at Skibbigeo. He had been watching anxiously for the boat and waiting for news. Thord could tell he was relieved to see father home safe and sound.

"What has happened?" he yelled from the shore. "We saw the beacons and some of our men went. They are not back yet. Do you have any news of them?"

"They are fine," shouted father. "All the Orcadians are fine."

"Thanks be to God," said Kettil, "but what happened?"

"I'll tell you when we come ashore," said father.

Sweyn and his sons helped to unload the wood and Kettil promised to look after it until they could come and fetch it with Hal. The caisies were swung ashore and they said their goodbyes to Sweyn and thanked him. Rain started to fall, just as Sweyn had thought it would, and they hurried to get the wood stacked inside the yard at Kettil's house.

"Come in," said Kettil. "There will be something ready for you to eat." Father bent his head and went in through the doorway.

When they had eaten the fish and bannocks that were set before them, Kettil asked once more to be told what had happened and father began telling him about the English invasion and the battle of Papdale. Kettil had been to Kirkwall once, to sell his fish, and he could remember the cathedral and the castle and the Bishop's Palace, but he had never been to the place where the women washed the clothes. Father explained where it was and what had happened during the battle.

"I've heard of Edward Sinclair, of course," said Kettil. "I don't think I ever saw him, though."

It was still raining when they left Kettil's house and set off across the land, beside the loch, towards home. Thord was tired. He had not slept much last night. He was still too aware of the battle and all the things that he had seen and he had lain sleepless for a long time. He was not going to let father see that he was tired, though, and he shouldered his caisie and tried to keep step while father strode along through the heather. Father must have seen how tired he was, though, for he slackened his step and put a hand out to help Thord with his caisie. Thord smiled up at him.

"We need to get home as quick as we can, faither," he said. "Don't we?"

"Yes, Dod, we do," said father. "They will be worrying."

It seemed to take forever to walk along the lochside, but at last the house came in sight. Thord brightened up a little and walked a little faster. As they came nearer the rain eased and the clouds began to roll back from the west. They looked and saw mother come running towards them with Christane stumbling along behind. Da was waving his stick and walking slowly down from the house to the loch shore.

"Magnus. Oh, Magnus. Thank goodness!" shouted mother.

"Faither! Dod! Have you brought my horsie?" shouted Christane.

"I knew it," said father. "We needn't have bothered to come home without that."

"We saw the beacons," said mother, hanging onto father's arm. "We knew there was trouble. We thought we might have lost you both."

"No, no, Ingirid," said father. "No chance of that." Thord said nothing but he remembered how he had thought the same thing. There was no point in telling mother, though.

"WHERE'S MY HORSIE?" yelled an insistent voice in their ears.

Everyone burst out laughing. Christane looked indignantly at all of them. Thord set down his caisie and hunted around inside it. He found the cloth for mother and unrolled it until he found the little red horse. When he handed it to Christane she gave a crow of delight and rushed to show it to Da.

"Look at my horsie!" she said. "See! Look at my peerie horsie!" and she hugged it to herself.

Lina came out through the door and said grumpily, "This is a fine time to get home. The dinner will be spoilt and we're having cock chicken."

The dinner was very good. They ate the chicken with oatmeal and beans from the creu. There was ale for father and bland for Thord. It was good to be home. Thord thought that mother's cooking was better than aunt Freda's, in spite of the spices and fancy wheat bread.

"Tell us," said Da. "Tell us what happened. They would not light the beacons unless it was serious. An invasion. An attack. Tell us."

"Father went in the battle," blurted out Thord. "I thought he would be killed." Tears started to his eyes. "He's wounded." Mother gasped.

"Shush!" said father. "It's not serious. It has nearly healed, thanks to Freda's ointment. All right, you can see it if you insist." He rolled up his sleeve to let mother look and she heaved a sigh of relief.

"Yes. You're right, Magnus. It is not too bad and it is healing well. How did you get this?"

Father said nothing for a time. Then he hunted in his caisie and produced the crown that Edward Sinclair had handed to him.

"This is for you, Da," he said. "From your friend, Edward Sinclair." Da looked at it in amazement.

"What on earth is that for?" he asked.

So father told him the story of the English invasion, of the battle and Edward Sinclair's part in it. Da listened intently and nodded his head now and then. He asked a great many questions about the cannon. He had heard of them but had never seen one.

"And where was Dod all this time?" asked mother at last.

"He was safe, Ingirid. Never worry. He was in the Bishop's palace with your friend George, Da."

"I don't know anyone called George," said Da, puzzled.

"He said to tell you that Thord Rendall was asking for you," said Thord. "It's the Kirkwall folk that call him George. He's called Dod, like me and you."

"Goodness me!" said Da. "Thord Rendall. Well I never! He was at Summerdale. He should have had a crown too, like me." Da looked at his coin. "You should have left this with Adam too," he said. "It's not much use here."

"You can give it to him next summer," said father. "They have promised to come." Mother looked pleased.

"That storm!" said mother. "I was wishing it anywhere but here for it was flattening the crops and it is coming near hairst. But it seems that it was meant to be! To drive away the English ships. And maybe the crop will be fine. It is standing well today and it is too soon for the grain to be shaken off."

"Come and show me," said father. They went out together to look at the fields.

Da turned to Thord and said, "Now maybe you can tell me what you would not tell your mother."

Thord looked around anxiously but Lina and Christane were outside on the brig-stones playing with Christane's horsie.

"You were right, Da," he said. "A battle is not exciting. It is terrible. I was so frightened and the cannon made such a terrible noise and I thought the walls might fall down. And I thought that faither would be killed and how would you and me look after Mam and Christane." Tears came to his eyes once more and Da put his arm round his shoulder and hugged him.

"Ow!" said Thord.

"What's this?" asked Da. "You weren't fighting, I hope, Dod?"

"No," said Thord, "but I did get this in the battle. It was George that did it. He held on to me so tight. He wanted me to go down into the palace but I couldn't. I had to see what was happening to faither, so he let me stay up there with him but he held on to me so tight. I didn't feel it at the time."

"Well, well," said Da. "I'm glad he was there. Thord Rendall! Well, well."

"What did you think of the cathedral, Dod?" his mother asked him later.

"I thought it was very grand," said Thord. "You can see it from a long way away. It's really big, isn't it? And it's nice inside, sort of quiet and airy, like the top of the hill or, or – I don't know. Special."

"I know what you mean," said his mother.

"I'm glad I was there," said Thord. He yawned. "I didn't like the battle, Mam, but I'm glad I was there all the same."

"Off to bed," said mother.

Thord fell asleep as soon as he lay down and no dreams troubled him.

Thursday, 30th September, 1557

Thord heard a voice saying, "Wake up, sleepyhead!" and felt someone shaking him. He struggled to open his eyes and peered up at a face. Father was laughing at him.

"Come on, Dod," he said. "It's time to bring in the last of the hairst. Hurry now! It's a good day for it."

Thord swung his feet to the floor, yawned, gave himself a shake and tied on his old rivlins. He would get new ones for the winter and it was still warm enough to run with bare feet but he found the cut straw sharp on his feet and thought he would cover them. He went through to the firehouse and breakfast, expecting to find Lina grumbling on as usual, but she was singing. He did not know what the tune was but she was trying her best.

Thord looked at his mother and nodded his head towards Lina.

"Last day of the hairst, Dod. Big supper tonight, remember?" Thord understood. Einar would be coming. And so would Karl and his mother, he thought, and Olaf too probably.

Thord finished his breakfast and followed father out to the stable to fetch out the oxen. Father led out two of them and Thord fetched the other two. They harnessed them as just as they had in the Voar for the ploughing but this time, of course, the oxen were pulling the sled to carry home the sheaves.

The weather had been kind to them this year. They had had a storm on the thirteenth of August but it had not done very much damage. The crop had grown up again, especially the oats which always sprang back quickly. Since then there had been very little wind so the grain had not shaken off the crops. And there had been a lot of sunshine so that the crops had ripened as they wanted.

They had begun the cutting a week or so before. Da had come out to cut some and Thord and Karl had cut quite a lot. They had done well, Thord thought. A lot of people had come to help. Father had been pleased when he saw the fields cut and each sheaf standing upright by itself with the bottom spread out to dry in the wind.

Some of the sheaves had fallen over, of course. If there was one that was not as thick, then it might fall over. Father took some of the thinner ones and leant them together, but they did not dry so quickly that way. But there had been no rain and all of the sheaves had dried well.

Thord had found the strip they had sown on Bogel Day easily. It had been a good idea to mark it with the big stones. Father and he had cut that bit together and they had made sure that those sheaves were in a safe place on their own until they were threshed and the grain stored for next Bogel Day. It had brought them good luck this year, with the weather. They had grown good crops.

The very first sheaf to be cut had already been threshed. The grain had been dried and mother had ground it on the quern-stones. She had made bursteen from it and Da had been the first to taste it. This was very important. If he said it was good and satisfying, then they would have enough to last the winter and more, and they would all have a happy year to come. And Da had said it was very good; better than last year's.

The last few days had been spent in hauling the sheaves into the yard and bigging them into skroos. Da helped as much as he could with the skroos and

Thord's job was to take the oxen out to the field with the sled, help to load it up and haul it back to the yard. Karl and his mother had been there every day, loading sheaves on, and sometimes Karl would take a turn with the oxen. He liked doing that. He said that he liked the way the oxen snorted when they were pulling hard.

Father had built most of the skroos, but he had let Thord try and he had shown him how to lay the sheaves so that the water would run off the skroos when it rained and not down into the middle of them. If water got into the middle, then the skroo would rot and they would lose the grain. So you had to be very careful about the way you laid the sheaves in rows.

Today it was not just Lina who was excited. Everyone was. It was a sunny, warm day and the last of the hairst was being led in. Everyone was laughing and chattering and it did not seem like work at all.

When Thord came back from the yard after hauling in the first load, he found Lina showing Christane how to twist roses from the straw. Lina's roses were neat and pretty. Christane's roses looked more like ragged robins but she was trying very hard, the tip of her tongue sticking out of the corner of her mouth.

"What are you going to do with these?" asked Thord.

"We'll decorate the house with them," said Lina.

"Better stick Christane's behind yours then," said Thord. Christane looked indignantly at him.

"Mine are good too," she said. "Just bigger than Lina's. I'm making a special one to put on my horsie."

Thord and Karl led the oxen back with another load. They seemed to be clearing the field quite fast. There were only a few loads left. They could help in the yard then. They pushed the load off the sled with the help of some of the people there and set off out again. Father shouted to Thord to remind him to leave the last sheaf on the field so that they could fetch it when everything else had been done. Thord remembered that they had to keep this last sheaf separate to give to Hal and the mare on New Year's Day. It was their special treat to thank them for all their work during the year.

When they came into the yard with the last load father came across and looked at the sheaves in it. He chose an especially fat one and told Thord and Karl to put it up on the roof of the barn.

"Be careful now," he said. "We don't want you falling off the roof."

Thord and Karl climbed up and set the sheaf firmly on the ridge and tied it there with some thin cord. Thord knew that this was to protect them against the trows. He was not sure what the trows would do to them if they did not have one of the last sheaves up there, but he did not want to find out by not putting it up. In any case, he and Karl enjoyed scrambling about on the roof. There was a different view of things from up there.

Olaf and his father arrived and helped to big the last of the skroos. Thord fetched the simmons that Da and father had made over last winter and everyone helped to tie the skroos down securely. It was a fine sight, Thord thought, to see the neat rows of skroos in the yard and to know that there would be plenty for them and for the animals over the winter and up to next hairst. There would be enough and to spare. Karl and his mother would not go hungry either this winter.

When the skroos were tied down and the yard was tidied up, everyone went out in a kind of procession to fetch in the last sheaf, the sheaf for Hal and the mare. It was carried back in triumph and set carefully in a corner of the barn.

Lina disappeared inside to help mother prepare the supper. Thord kicked off his rivlins and ran down to the burn. He and Olaf and Karl had a fine time splashing their feet, and themselves. Thord saw Christane coming down and hoped that she would not fall in again. It was not so warm now. But she had come to tell them that the food was ready and they ran back up to the house.

Einar had arrived and Thord could see Eyvind with his gue under his arm. The firehouse was packed with people and Lina and mother were very busy handing out bannocks and cheese, and plates of smoked trout and reestit mutton. There was kale too, and some turnips from the creu. Thord wondered if there would be enough ale in the kirn for everyone. He saw Father Harald sitting beside father on Da's bed and went over to speak to him.

"I'm sorry I haven't been to see you to do my reading, Father," he said, "but we've been very busy with the hairst."

"That's fine, Dod," said Father Harald. "The hairst has to come first just now. I know that. This is really splendid ale that Ingirid makes. And the food is very good. I can't remember when I had such a fine supper." Mother heard him and looked pleased.

Thord went to help mother hand round the food. He was hungry so not all of it got handed round. Some of it disappeared inside Thord. He saw Christane sitting in a corner by herself with a bannock piled high with trout and mutton and cheese.

"I hope she doesn't burst," he thought.

There were people to be fed outside on the brig-stones as well. Thord was kept busy for quite a while, but eventually everyone seemed to have had enough and mother and Lina and himself could rest. People drifted outside and Eyvind took up his gue and started to play. Before long almost everyone had joined in a ring-dance. Eyvind's playing followed the singing and the steps of the dance. Thord saw father and mother join in. He looked around for Christane. He thought she might like to join in too, but she was fast asleep on Da's bed.

"Come on Karl," he said. "We can do this too." He seized Karl's arm and dragged him into the circle.

"I don't know the words," said Karl.

"Doesn't matter. I don't either but we can learn them. Come on."

When the light faded, late in the evening, everyone crowded into the firehouse again. Karl's mother sang a ballad while mother handed round more food and drink. Lina was nowhere to be seen, but Thord could not see Einar either. He thought they must be outside somewhere. He helped mother again.

"A story! A story!" someone shouted to Da.

"Aha!" said Da. "I know the very one. I'll tell you about the fiddler who played at the hairst home supper. I don't know if his name was

Eyvind, but it could well have been that. So I will call him Eyvind, and he was a very fine fiddler."

Someone shouted out through the door, "Hey, Eyvind! Come and listen to this, beuy!"

"He played all night at the supper," said Da, "and then he thought it was time he went home. But as he was going home, he passed a knowe and from inside it he heard music. And such fine music. He stopped to listen.

"And then suddenly a door opened in the side of the knowe and the music got louder and light streamed out. Eyvind looked inside and there were many peerie folk dancing in a ring and two or three fiddlers playing some tunes that Eyvind had never heard before. He poked his head inside to listen better. He wanted to learn the tunes.

"Soon one of the fiddlers came over to him and said, 'Why don't you join in?' so Eyvind took up his gue and started playing. He found to his amazement that he could play all of the new tunes he was hearing, easily. He played and played. More and better tunes rang out from his gue and the peerie men crowded round shouting 'Well done! Well done!'

"He played faster and faster. His fingers ran like lightning over the strings. Faster and faster went the dancers. Eyvind's head was spinning and it seemed to him that all the peerie men were spinning round and round with him. With the music still ringing in his ears he fell into a faint and crumpled up on the ground.

"When he woke, he was lying outside the knowe, his gue beside him. There was no sign of the door although he hunted and hunted. The sun was high in the sky and he thought he must have slept for a while. He took up his gue and walked home.

"When he reached home, he saw his wife hurrying out of the door to meet him. 'What am I going to say?' he thought. 'I never came home last night. She will be so angry."

"Hear that Eyvind?" said a voice. "Your wife will give you a right telling off."

"She did," said Da. "She said 'Where have you been all this time.'

"'Well,' said Eyvind, 'I was playing at the hairst home supper at Kirkbuster.'

"'That was a year and a day ago,' said his wife. 'Nobody has seen you since then. Where have you been?'

"'But that was just yesterday,' said Eyvind, puzzled. 'I spent last night with the peerie folk, learning new tunes.'

"'Spent last year, more like,' said his wife.

"Eyvind never understood how he came to miss a whole year, but he remembered all the new tunes and played them ever after."

Thord thought that that was one of the best stories that he had heard Da telling. It seemed everyone else liked it too. Even Eyvind seemed to have enjoyed it, but he said to Da that he would not mind learning some new tunes if Da would just tell him where this knowe was.

The daylight was creeping in through the liora before the last of the guests went home. Christane was still asleep on Da's bed so father carried her through to her own bed and Thord followed. He knew he would sleep well. The hairst was in, they had had a great evening and maybe Da would tell them that story again sometime. After all, Christane would need to hear it. She had been asleep all through it.

Sunday, 31st October, 1557

Thord lay in his bed listening to the familiar morning sounds from the firehouse. He could hear the scrape and rattle as his mother raked out the peat fire and took the ashes away from the back. She would put them in the byre to add to the dung. He could hear Lina turning the quern-stone, grinding bere to make into bursteen. He could hear a knock or two coming from the byre as the kye got up to see what was happening. He could hear a clatter from the other side, from the stable.

"That will be Hal," he thought, "waiting to see if anyone will give him his breakfast."

He could hear a cluck or two from the hens as his father went out through the door to see what the weather was like. It had been a long warm summer and a good hairst but late in September there were gales.

"Terran's trying to get the upper hand again," Da had said. "There will be a fight and the Sea Mither will have to go away again. And then we're back into winter."

All the familiar morning sounds crowded in on Thord and suddenly he felt gloriously happy. Since the battle in August he had felt upset, anxious, worried. If invaders could come twice, they could come again. Of course, they had been beaten twice as well. So they could be beaten a third time, and in the meantime he was at home, safe. And tonight was Halloween. Tomorrow, for Hallowmas, there would be a feast but tonight there would be a lot of fun.

The light was struggling through the liora when he went into the firehouse to get his breakfast. The coly lamp was still alight but as the daylight grew stronger, mother put it out. His father came back in and said that he did not think that the day was fair enough to put the kye out on the meadowland and they would just feed them inside.

"It's going to rain soon. The cloud is heavy and the wind is getting up. Come and help me feed the horses and the oxen first, Dod."

Thord went out onto the brigstones and looked up at the sky. Yesterday had been bright, the autumn sunlight slanting golden on the land. He had watched the skeins of geese arrowing through the air, honking noisily before landing on the empty cornfields. Today the geese were flying higher and heading southwards. He could hear the noise of them over the rising wind.

As the day wore on the wind became stronger and blew rain before it. It was much colder now and Thord was glad of his new rivlins which father had made for him. They were made of sheepskin with the fleece inside keeping his feet warm. If the rain lasted a long time and turned everything to mud, he would need to wrap his rivlins in straw when he went out to keep his feet dry.

Evening came and Olaf and his father arrived to share a meal with them. Mother kept looking out of the door. She said that old Osla, the wise-woman, was coming. She did not have so far to come, just a mile or so, but she walked slowly and stiffly and mother was worried that she might be finding it too cold. Lina was even more anxious, which Thord thought a bit strange. But he thought too that it might be because Lina wanted her future told and Osla was good at that.

Osla arrived just as mother had dinner ready. She was cold, she said, and mother dragged a stool up to the fire for her to sit on and gave her a plate of mutton and kale. Lina hovered over her, asking her if she was warm enough now and if she wanted more to eat. Olaf nudged Thord in the ribs and winked at him.

"Have you had enough, Osla?" asked Lina for the umpteenth time.

"Plenty, lass, plenty, thank you," said Osla. Lina still hovered, hopping from one foot to the other.

"Now," said Osla, "maybe one of you wants their fortune told."

"Yes, me," said Lina quickly and Thord saw his mother grin and Da's eyes were twinkling.

"I'll need an egg," said Osla. Mother took one from her precious store in the jar of vinegar. "Hope it's a good one," said Osla.

Lina fetched a bowl with some water and Osla broke the egg into it, keeping the yolk out. She swirled the egg and water till it looked bubbly and then set it down in the hearth. She passed her hands over the bowl a few times, muttering to herself the while.

"Ah!" she said. "I see a fine lad here for you. This will be the lad you're going to marry."

"What does he look like?" said Lina, desperately hoping that he had fair hair like Einar and a curly beard.

"Well, now," said Osla. "Wait till I see. He's tall." Lina nodded her head.

"And he's got fair hair," said Osla. Lina nodded her head so vigorously that Thord thought it might fall off.

"To be sure of who it is," said Osla, "you might want to hear his voice. And maybe you can do that too, if you do what I tell you."

"What do I have to do?" said Lina eagerly.

"Take a clew of wool that you have spun yourself," said Osla.

"That will be easy," thought Thord. When they were not busy with anything else, his mother and Lina would card wool and spin it on a spindle. Thord thought his mother could do it with her eyes shut, as she never looked at the wool or the spindle when she was spinning. Her fingers did it all. Lina was nearly as good at it.

Lina went over to her neuk bed and rummaged around till she found a good-sized clew.

"Now you must take that out to the barn," said Osla, "and then you throw it in the kiln and say, 'Who takes hold of my clew's end?' And then you will hear the voice of your future husband." Lina nodded and muttered to herself, "Who takes hold of my clew's end? Right." And off out the door she went. Olaf nudged Thord again and hissed, "Come on!" He shot through to the sallur, through to the stable and into the barn. Thord followed.

"Shush!" said Olaf and they hid behind one of the grain baskets. They were just in time, for they could hear Lina coming in through the outside door. She left the door open so a glimmer of light came in. They could see her going over to the kiln. Then she threw the clew in and said, fearfully, "Who takes hold of my clew's end?"

"I do!" said Einar's voice.

"Aaah!" screamed Lina and blundered her way out through the door, yelling her way all along the brig-stones. "Wait, Lina. Wait!" shouted Einar, climbing out of the kiln. He tripped over something and fell. Muttering something, he struggled to his feet, still shouting to Lina to wait.

Olaf and Thord were giggling so hard that Thord thought they must have heard them in Kirkwall, let alone across the barn floor, but Einar paid no heed to them as he shot out of the door after Lina.

Suddenly there was an even bigger screech from Lina and she came running back along the brig-stones, bumping into Einar and giving another screech. Einar fell again and Lina fell on top of him. Olaf and Thord, watching from the doorway, held their sides and burst out laughing. An orange glare lit up Einar and Lina struggling on the ground, trying to get up.

"Help!" said Olaf. "What's that?" Thord looked out of the doorway and almost screeched as loud as Lina. Coming along the Brig-stones were three strange figures clad in straw skirts to their knees and tall pointed straw hats covering their heads and faces. They were carrying flaring torches and through the two holes in their hats Thord could see the glint of eyes.

"Oh, my," said Thord. "What? What?"

"Beuy, Einar, what's happened to you?" said one of the straw men.

"You frightened the life out of her, that's what," said Einar.

"I don't know if we're to blame," said another straw man. "She was screeching her head off before she saw us. Something else had frightened her."

Einar said nothing. He helped Lina up and the two of them followed the straw men into the house.

"It's the skeklers," said Olaf. "That last one was Eyvind with his gue. Come on. We'll go back through the other way."

They sped back through the house and emerged into the fire house to hear Da saying, "You're welcome here this Halloween, boys. You'll need something to eat."

Mother turned to Thord and said, "Take this plate over to Eyvind, Dod." Thord took the plate thinking that no-one had noticed that he and Olaf were missing. He thought it might be better if they said nothing about it. Einar might be angry with them for hiding in the barn. He handed over the plate and looked for Olaf to tell him to keep quiet. At first he could not see him and then he noticed a heaving lump on Da's bed. Olaf had his head buried in Da's blanket to stifle his laughing.

Eyvind tuned up his gue and Olaf gradually stopped laughing. He drew nearer to Eyvind. Eyvind turned his head and saw him.

"Right, Olaf," he said. "Let's see what you can do." He handed the gue to Olaf. Thord gaped. Olaf took hold of the gue and began to play. It was a bit squeaky and some of the notes sounded a bit funny but he played on and at the end everyone was shouting, "Go on, Olaf. Keep it up."

Olaf beamed. He handed the gue back to Eyvind.

"I didn't know you could play!" said Thord.

"I've been learning," said Olaf. "Eyvind's teaching me. He's helping father to make a gue for me. Have to make sure it sounds right."

"Olaf's clever," said Christane. "He can make a tune."

Thord was happy. The house was full of noise and warmth.

"Maybe I like the evening best," he thought, "when we're all sitting round the fire and there's talking and laughing. I think I like the evening best."

He sighed and wondered if he should try and learn to play the gue too. Maybe Olaf would teach him.

Yule
Monday, 20th December, 1557 – Tammasmas E'en

Thord lay cosily in bed. He knew he should get up but whenever he pushed his arm out from under the blankets he could feel the cold in the room. There had been flurries of snow the day before and father had been a bit worried about the sheep. He and Thord had taken Ben and gone to round them up off the hill and take them inside the dyke. It had been cold work and Thord had been shivering by the time they got home again. But now the sheep were safe inside the dyke until the weather got better.

Thord could hear his mother clearing out the fire and building it up again. He could hear Da coughing too. Father came in from outside, stamping his straw-clad rivlins to shake the snow off them.

"It's still fairly dark," he said, "but the sky looks full of snow. We'd best get the animals fed as soon as we can. We need to take in some hay from the yard and some sheaves for threshing. This is the first day of Yule so we need to have enough in the barn to last over the whole of Yule."

Thord plucked up courage and got out of bed. He shivered for a bit but when he had put on his tunic and his cosy, fleecy rivlins he began to feel warm again. He left Christane still sleeping and went through to the firehouse. Da was eating his bursteen and drinking a bowl of Axes-drink. Mother had warmed it in front of the fire.

When Thord had eaten his breakfast, he went out with his father to fetch the hay and sheaves into the barn. If they could take in enough to last all of Yule then they would not need to go outside again if the weather was bad. They would have to make sure the sheep had enough to eat, though. But maybe the snow would not last that long.

They worked hard for most of the morning, shifting hay and sheaves, feeding kye and sheep and finally threshing some sheaves. The wind was bitter and blowing strongly and Thord was glad to get into the barn. Father took a couple of sheaves and laid them on the rounded clay strip in the middle of the barn, between the doors. He and Thord took a flail each and began to hit the sheaves. Thump went father's flail followed by a thump from Thord's. They beat in a steady rhythm until the grain slid away from the straw. They piled the straw at one side and began again with two fresh sheaves.

It was hard work but it made Thord feel warm and the heat spread even to his toes. When they had a good heap of grain father opened the back door wide and the front door slightly to let in the wind and they tossed the grain to get rid of the chaff. They scooped it up at last and piled it into the grain caisie. And went to see if mother had some food ready.

"We have to do a lot today, Dod," said father, with his mouth full of bannock and cheese. "We must make sure that the trows can't do us any mischief over Yule and next year. When the sun sets we'll make the yard safe first."

When sunset came father pulled two straws from a skroo in the yard and laid them in the gateway in the shape of a cross.

"That should protect the crop," he said.

He pulled a hair from each cow and ox and one each from Hal and the mare. These hairs he pleated carefully and fastened them above the door into the byre.

"That should keep the animals safe," he said.

Finally he took a burning peat from the fire and carried it from end to end of the steading, from the byre, through the house, through the stable and into the barn, and then back again.

"That should look after the steading and all the people in it," he said.

Da nodded his head.

"You've done that right," he said. "We should be fine now."

Christane was coughing. The smoke from the peat had made her eyes water.

"Mam," she said, "I think I need some Axes-drink. I'm coughing."

"I think a drink of water would be fine," said mother. Christane scowled.

"Come, Lina," said mother. "We must put away the wool and the cards and the spindles now till after Yule."

"Oh, I know that," said Lina. "I've put mine away already, but I don't understand really why we have to do it."

"Well, we have to do it because Magnus owns sheep. It would not be right for us to card or spin over Yule. And it would be very bad luck. Anyway, you know what they say."

"No. What?" asked Lina.

"A woman must not spin any longer than Tammasmas or she will lose her thumb. You don't want that, do you?"

"No!" said Lina, shaking her head.

"Now we're ready for Yule," said father.

Thord was looking forward to it.

Saturday, 25th December, 1557 – Christmas Day

Thord woke on Yule morning to the sound of Eyvind and his gue. He was playing the tune called 'Day Dawn' which was special to this day. It was a lovely tune and he knew it was going to be a special day when he heard that.

He scrambled out of bed quickly and hurried through to the firehouse. It was still dark and the coly-lamp had been lit. Mother was beginning to make the breakfast and father had already started to feed the kye as the animals had to be fed before daybreak. The weather had been cold, snowy and windy and Thord was glad that they had taken in enough fodder for the animals before Yule. They could feed them now without going outside.

Eyvind came in through the door, stamping his feet and shaking the snow off his clothes.

"Come and warm yourself, Eyvind," said mother, "before you make for the next house. I've warmed a cog of ale for you and there's a bannock and cheese." She handed it to him and Eyvind took it gratefully.

"The snow has eased off a bit," he said, "and the wind is not so strong now. It might fair up later on." He drank his ale and disappeared out of the door again to visit the next house with his fine tune.

Thord helped father to feed all the animals and then they sat down to their own breakfast.

"When it is daylight, we can see what the day is like before we go to the kirk. Father Harald is expecting all of us but the weather will have to be much better before Da can go, I think."

"If Hal can go, I can go," said Da, coughing a little.

"Hmm!" said father.

With the daylight came the sun, blinking through the liora and making their hearts soar. After so many dark days, it seemed like a special gift and Thord looked out over a silvery white landscape. The burn ran like a dark thread in front of him, making its way to the loch. If the weather stayed cold and snowy like this, the loch might freeze at the edges and they could slide over it. That would be fun.

The wind eased too almost to nothing and Hal was pleased to be out. Da piled on some extra coats and climbed onto Hal's back and they set off for the kirk. For once Lina did not grumble very much, although she did complain that she thought her toes might drop off. She liked the Yule service very much, and besides Einar would be there and he was coming back to Kirkbuster afterwards for the feast.

It was a happy service and everyone came out after with big smiles on their faces. Christane had loved it all, especially the manger story.

"It must have been just like our house," she said, "with all the animals around. Just think! When I was born it was just the same as that baby, wasn't it, Mam?"

"Well, a bit maybe," said mother. "It's nice to have the animals near."

Many of the young men followed them home to Kirkbuster. They were going to play the Ba game and it was usually played in their district near Kirkbuster. Thord wished he were old enough to join in

"Maybe next year," he thought. "I'll be ten then. That should be big enough."

Olaf and his father were with them too. Olaf's father joined in the game, but Olaf was not allowed to, although he made a valiant attempt to join them.

"No, no, Olaf," said his father. "Not for a few years yet."

They all stood and watched the game, even Da. Father stood and watched for a while. He kept saying things like, "No, that's not the way to do it," and "Oh, can you not do better than that." Suddenly he said, "Oh, somebody needs to show them the right way," and he dived off to join the game. Da burst out laughing.

"Oh, I can remember feeling like that too," he said, and chuckled to himself.

Einar gave the ba a huge kick up in the air and it went far higher than anyone else had managed to kick it. Lina laughed and clapped her hands.

"He's the best at this," she said. "Nobody will beat that!" Thord was sure his father could do better and he waited to see what he would do. Soon the ba came near to where father was standing and he ran towards it and kicked hard. His feet in the rivlins bound with straw slipped and he missed the ba completely and sat down with a wallop.

"Oh, no," thought Thord. "That was terrible." He saw Olaf laughing and scowled at him, but then he heard a louder laugh behind him and he turned to see mother standing there, pointing her finger at his father and shouting, "That showed them, Magnus, eh?" Father got up ruefully and shook his head with a grin on his face.

"Why was faither sitting down, Mam?" asked Christane.

"Maybe he's tired," said mother.

The game carried on until it was growing dark. Einar had won with his huge kick and Lina was very proud of him. She kept asking everyone if they had seen Einar kick the ba so high it nearly disappeared and Einar got a little embarrassed about it.

The house filled with people as the players and the watchers trooped off the field. There was not enough room for everyone so Thord and father cleared the barn, pushing everything to the sides and the barn filled up too. Mother produced some candles that she had made in the summer from the beeswax and lit them in the kitchen. Christane stared around in delight. Thord thought there was so much light, it could have been daytime.

Coly-lamps were lit in the barn. They made the barn look huge and mysterious, the roof soaring into shadow. Thord remembered the roof of St. Magnus which seemed as if it was as high as the sky.

Mother and Lina had plenty of help to hand round the food. All of the women who were there helped them and went back and fore with plates piled high with mutton and smoked trout and a goose roasted slowly in the front of the fire. There were hens to eat too and Da tried to tell Christane that one of them was Lotta, but Christane did not believe him.

"Da! Da! Look! There's Lotta sitting on the hallan there, see?" said Christane and she pointed to Lotta who was clucking sleepily and opening one eye at them. Da laughed.

When the feast had been eaten and the ale drunk, Eyvind fetched his gue again and as many as possible crowded into the barn and the dancing began. Thord saw Olaf going across to Eyvind and asking him something. Eyvind nodded and soon Thord saw Olaf produce his own gue and join in the music. Mother took Thord and Christane with her into the ring and they joined in, trying to sing the words and watch the steps at the same time. Christane hung onto father's arm and swung her feet off the ground. Father laughed.

Thord was determined to stay awake until the end of the dancing, although he knew it would be almost daybreak the next day. He was sure that he could do it.

He did not feel sleepy at all. In a break in the dancing, when someone was singing a ballad, he went across to Olaf and said, "Where did you get that gue?"

"I told you," said Olaf. "Father and Eyvind made it for me and father gave me it today. Great, eh?"

"You can play it well now," said Thord.

"No, not really," said Olaf, "but I will."

In spite of being determined to stay awake Thord began to feel sleepy. He saw Olaf rubbing his eyes as well, and Karl too. Christane was in bed already and Thord did not want to go through to the sallur. He pointed to a pile of sheaves in the corner. Olaf and Karl nodded and they all lay down on them.

"Just for a rest, mind," said Olaf.

"Yes, yes," said Thord. "It's just for a rest."

Soon after father looked across and then nudged mother and pointed. Three very happy tired boys were sound asleep on the sheaves. The music echoed around them and the dancers whirled past. Each had a smile on his face.

Saturday, 1st January, 1558 – New Year's Day

Thord heard father get up out of bed. He heard him shiver with the cold as he hauled on his tunic and strapped on his rivlins. He could hear mother through in the firehouse raking out the ashes and Da saying to her, "A good New Year to you Ingirid."

Father went through the door and wished Da a good New Year. Thord scrambled into his clothes and followed him. He wanted to see if there had been more snow so he opened the front door a little and looked out. The snow had gone and rain was falling from the dark sky. He shut the door quickly and came back to the fire.

Lina was getting out of her neuk bed, grumbling away as usual, but she brightened up when somebody said "A good New Year" and went away to fetch some bere to grind. Mother filled the pot with water and the day had begun.

It was still raining so father and Thord went through the house to the barn. They fetched the sheaf that had been kept for Hal and the mare, the last sheaf off the field in the hairst and they shared it between the horses. Hal threw back his head and whinnied.

"He's saying thank you, isn't he, faither?" said Thord.

"I think maybe he is, Dod," said father.

They went back and fore through the steading feeding the animals and did not bother to go outside. The light in the liora was growing stronger as they finished all the usual tasks and Thord came back to the fire to find Christane eating a bannock and cheese.

"Can I have some too, Mam?" he asked. Mother handed him a warm bannock and carried on baking them on the fire. Lina took it from him, spread some butter on it and put a lump of cheese on top. Thord thanked her and sat down to eat.

"Now," said father, "this is the start of the New Year so we must make sure that we do things right today. We must each of us do a little of the work that we will be doing for the rest of the year, just to make sure that we have good luck with it. Dod, come and help me twist a simmon, just a bit of it."

Thord went and fetched some straw from the barn and he and father twisted a yard or two of rope from it.

"That's fine, Dod," said father. "That will do us today. We can do some more tomorrow. From now until Uphelli Day we must mix the work with the celebrations. After that it will be back to work as usual, but for now we can enjoy ourselves.

Mother and Lina took some wool and Lina carded some while mother used her spindle. Da took the knife and some wood and made one or two harrow teeth. Everyone made sure that they did a little.

It was still raining but mother needed some water so Thord braved the weather and went down to the well near the side of the burn. He fetched several tubs of water and filled the big tub on the bink. There would be enough to do until tomorrow, he thought. Just when he was carrying in the last tubful he heard a sound of singing and peering through the rain he saw a group of men coming towards the house. He ran inside to tell father.

"It's the menyie-singers, faither," he said. "They're just coming up the brig-stones now."

Father went out to greet the men and tell them to hurry inside out of the wet and cold. Mother lit the coly lamp on the bracket on the wall and it shed a thin fitful light in the firehouse. She fetched a few of the candles that she had left and soon the room glowed and the shadows danced in the flickering light.

"There," said mother. "That's almost the last of the candles to welcome in the New Year. I just have one or two left for Candlemas."

Thord saw Eyvind in the group of men, and Einar was there as well. Then he saw Olaf. He was carrying his gue and looking very proud of himself.

"I can play with them now," he said. "I've practised a lot and they're letting me play with them." His father turned and smiled.

"He's getting quite good," he said. "His singing is terrible, of course. That's why we let him play the gue."

"Come on, Olaf," said Eyvind. "We need to give these lazy singers a start or they will never get going." He struck up a tune and Olaf followed. The men began to sing.

"Guid be tae this buirdly bigging,
"We're a' St Mary's men,
"Fae the steethe stane tae the rigging,
"Fore wur lady."

Thord listened carefully to the words of the verses. He would have liked to join in the singing, but he thought he had better not. There were a lot of verses.

"May a' your yowes be weel tae lamb,
"We're a' St Mary's men,
"And every ane hae a yowe and a ram,
"Fore wur lady."

He heard them singing a verse about his father and then one about his mother. They were laughing. Da was clapping his hands. "Go on," he said. "Go on!"

"Whar is the servant lass o this hoose?
"We're a' St Mary's men,
"Whar is she, that lass?
"Fore wur lady."

"Eh?" said Lina. "What's this?" She looked startled and Einar gave a huge laugh.

"And why is she no' as before,
"We're a' St Mary's men,
"In sweepin oot the ashes?
"Fore wur lady," sang the men.

"Well I never," said Lina. "Singing about me! What next!"

There were a great many verses in the song and everyone enjoyed it, either singing or listening. When the men had almost finished their song, there was a verse which made Da laugh and clap again;

"This is the best that we can tak,
"We're a' St Mary's men,
"And we will drink till wur lugs crack,
"Fore wur lady."

Eyvind finished playing with a flourish and clapped Olaf on the back.

"You did very well indeed," he said. "Must be my good teaching!"

"I think I need a drink after that," said Olaf hopefully, looking at mother as she carried a cog full of ale to the men.

"You can taste it," said Olaf's father, Jon. Olaf grabbed the cog and lifted it to his mouth. Jon took hold of the other side and stopped him drinking more than a very little. Olaf spluttered.

"I don't know if I really like that all that much," he said. The men laughed.

"Come, Olaf," said mother. "I have a little bland for you if you would like that."

"Yes, please," said Olaf.

Lina and mother handed round food, mutton and goose, bannocks and butter and cheese, and ale to drink. The firehouse was full and warm and soon someone was singing an old ballad. Da was asked for a story and he told them of the Great Selkie of Sule Skerry. It was a very good story, Thord thought, but a very sad one too. He was glad when Eyvind began a cheerful tune and the men joined in singing a merry song.

"Well, boys," said Eyvind, "we'd better get going. We have some other houses to visit before night yet."

Thord looked out through the door. The rain had gone and the sky had cleared. There was no moonlight to guide them as the new moon had arrived the day before. Eyvind produced a torch and lit it at the fire before they went out. He held it up and the rest followed him outside. They shouted farewell as they went over the brig-stones and onto the next house.

Thord sighed happily as he came back into the firehouse. He would have liked to go with them as Olaf was doing, but it was warm and familiar round the fire and maybe they could persuade Da to tell another story. But Christane was before him.

"Can we have another story, Da, please?" she asked. "Only can we have a happy one this time?" Everyone laughed, even Lina who was sulking a little because Einar had gone with the rest of the men. She had hoped he would stay behind.

So Da told them a happy and funny story, about a hogboon and the tricks he played on a cross old woman.

"Lina had better watch out," thought Thord. "If she keeps on grumbling the hogboon will come and play tricks on her." He looked around happily. There were another two weeks of Yule to come, with feasts and dancing and company, before Uphelli Day and the end of the celebration. And there would be a bonfire on Uphelli Day to welcome back the sun. It would be a good New Year.

Monday, 18th January, 1558 – Uphelli Day

When Thord came through to the firehouse on the morning of Uphelli Day, the sun was sending a thin trickle of light down through the liora, battling against the billowing smoke from the newly-banked fire. Lina was singing away while she ground the bere and mother was filling the pot with water.

Father was already working and he came in through the door with an armful of hay for the kye. "Cluck" went the sleepy hens as he walked under them and they stirred on the hallan. Thord could see Lotta's little beady eye watching, waiting to see if they were going to be fed as well.

Christane came through to the firehouse clutching her little wooden horsie. The paint was wearing off and it was looking a bit battered but it was still her favourite thing. Thord had set his little blue and white one in the recess in the wall above Da's bed. Da liked to look at it. He said that it reminded him of a horse that he had had when he was young. It had been a small horse but really strong and Da had ridden it over the hills and far away, he said.

This day was the last of the Yule days. They had enjoyed these Yule days very much. Although they had been careful to do a little work each day, there had been many visits from other people and there had been dancing and singing and story-telling. It had been a very good Yule, but now they had to begin the year's work; first the ploughing, then the sowing and then the reaping. They year stretched long in front of Thord.

This last day of Yule was therefore very special. It was a last holiday before getting down to work. It was goodbye to the old year and welcome to the new. It was goodbye to the darkest days of winter and welcome to the return of the sun.

There were shouts from outside and Thord ran out into the pale clear sunlight. Olaf was coming up the brig-stones and yelling to Thord to follow him out to the Ba field. The young men were there already beginning the game and Olaf wanted to watch.

"They might let me play next year, so I need to watch to see what to do," said Olaf.

Thord thought that even if they watched it might still be difficult to see what to do as the ba itself seldom appeared in sight, except when one of the men tried to kick it as high as possible. The rest of the time it was hidden by the men struggling to get hold of it.

As they reached the field the ba sailed high in the air.

"Bet that's Einar," said Olaf. "He's the best."

Einar appeared, lifted high on the shoulders of some of the men with the rest cheering him. Thord heard someone clapping their hands behind him and he looked round to see Lina standing there. Mother was there too watching and Thord looked anxiously to see if he could see father. He hoped that father would just watch the game this time.

He hoped in vain, for there was father and Olaf's father, Jon, in the middle of the game again. Jon got the ba and kicked as hard as he could. The ba rose high up, but not as high as Einar had kicked it.

"I hope faither doesn't get the ba," thought Thord. "He'll fall again." He watched intently to see if he could see where the ba was. He thought he had caught sight of it in front of Eyvind and he was waiting to see who would kick it next.

Suddenly Einar came running up and tried to grab the ba again. He was reaching out for it when he tripped over a tussock of last year's grass and fell flat on his face. Thord heard a strange noise. It reminded him a little of the noise that the cannon had made but not so loud.

"Einar, man, look what you've done!" yelled Eyvind as Einar struggled to his feet. Everyone looked. In front of Einar was a squashed flat ba, burst as he fell on it. There were groans from the rest of the men. They did not know if they could find another sheep's bladder to blow up inside the leather case. However they were lucky as someone had brought a spare one with them in case it was needed and soon the game was in full swing again.

Thord saw his father try to kick the ba. He bit his lip and clenched his fists and watched. To his relief the ba sailed in the air, almost as high as Einar's kick and there were shouts of "Well done, Magnus." Thord turned a smiling face towards his mother and saw that she was laughing. Lina was looking a bit annoyed, until she realised that Einar's kick was still the best.

The men played on until the light began to fail and then the players left the field, most of them to go home. Some came to Kirkbuster with father and mother and Lina made sure that Einar was one of them. She rushed ahead to start getting the dinner ready.

The wind was rising a little and it had swung round from the north to the west. Thord thought that they would probably have rain tomorrow. It was good, though, that it had stayed fine for Uphelli Day. He hoped that the rain would not come before the bonfire at night.

They went into the firehouse to be met by clouds of smoke. Lina had built up the fire before she noticed that the wind had changed and the firehouse had filled with smoke before she could shift the skylan board round. She had the pole in her hands but she was coughing and spluttering. Father reached up and changed the board round and the smoke began to go up through the liora again.

Some of the men had brought torches with them and as soon as they had finished eating, they lit the torches.

"Now we have to chase out the trows," said father. The men went from the firehouse to the byre and chased out Lina.

"Ha!" thought Thord. "Lina's a trow!" The torches went to the stable next and Hal snorted at them. Then father led them into the barn where they chased out Einar. "Another trow!" thought Thord. "No wonder Lina likes him!"

When they had chased out all the trows and made sure that they would have a trouble-free year, the men set off towards the bonfire site. Everyone followed except Da.

"Too cold for me," he said. "I'll stay here in the warm and Ben can stay with me."

They left Da and Ben looking warm and comfortable in front of the fire and walked down over the brig-stones. The sky was clear and the moon shone silver on the water of the loch. It was four days past the full moon but there was plenty of light.

They could see little lines of light coming from all directions, orange lines that bobbed and swayed. Soon the lines grew bigger as more men joined each one. Then it seemed as if there was one long line pointing towards the bonfire site and flowing onwards. A ring of light circled round and then the torches were hurled into the bonfire and the red flames rose in the air. Everyone cheered.

"The sun is coming back now," thought Thord. He watched the lively sparks fly up from the bonfire, lifted by the fresh wind. He looked around at his father and mother. Christane was holding onto mother's hand very tightly. The heat from the bonfire warmed them all, just as the heat from the peat fire on the back kept them all warm as they sat in a circle round it.

When the bonfire died down everyone left to go home. Father carried Christane as she was too tired to walk. Lina held onto Einar's hand tightly and dragged him back with her to Kirkbuster.

Da was dozing in front of the fire when they went into the house, his right hand on Ben's head. Mother and Lina fetched bannocks and butter and cheese and poured ale for father and Einar. Mother gave Da some Axes-drink. They sat round the familiar fire, warm and happy, as the wind rose outside and whirled the smoke up through the lIora. Thord could see everyone's face shining in the light from the fire.

"Soon it will be Candlemas again and my birthday," he thought. "Da will say, 'I'll give you a good wish from old Dod to peerie Dod.' I'll be ten and just about grown-up. There will be nothing I can't do when I'm ten."

GLOSSARY

Axes	illness characterised by a cough
Axes-girse	plant used to cure Axes, dandelion
Ba	ball; game still played in Kirkwall at Christmas and New Year
Bairn	child
Bannocks	form of bread, round, baked on a flat stone or griddle
Bere	from O.E. bære, old form of barley
Beulding	gathering, putting in a pen
Beuy	Orcadian greeting equal to man or 'mate'. Never said to women.
Bink	bench, shelf, usually made of stone
Bland	drink made from dropping hot stone into buttermilk. It results in a clear liquid which sparkles
Bogel Day	17th March, old calendar; day to sow some seed to ensure a good harvest
Boor-trees	elder trees
Brae	hillside; slope
Brig-stones	large, flat stones laid as a path in front of the house
Broch	prehistoric circular stone tower
Brose Day	Shrove Tuesday
Brough	stronghold
Brunnie	round, thick scone
Buddo	term of endearment for a child
Bursteen	grains of bere parched and then ground
Bus-herra	red-coloured stone set at sun side of door for good luck
Caisie	large basket woven from straw
Clew	ball of wool
Clibber saddle	wooden saddle made from two pieces of board pinned together at the top
Coles	large heaps of straw or hay
Coly-lamp	bowl of fish-oil with a wick hanging over the edge
Couples	rafters
Creu	small area of land enclosed by a wall for growing vegetables or using as a pen for animals
Cubbie	basket made of woven straw
Dian-stone	small red stone hung on sun side of plough
Dickie-doo	Hide and Seek; probably from Old Norse 'dikka thu'
Dochan	dock plant
Droo	kind of seaweed like long thin threads
Eccle-girse	butterwort
Eetches	hoes
Fairing	gift brought back from a fair
Fairy	supernatural creature generally malevolent, but with no wings
Firehouse	main room of the house with the fire in it
Fletties	large mats woven from straw
Fowerern	boat rowed by four oars

Geo	inlet of the sea
Goar	used only in phrase 'Goar Vellyie', autumn battle or struggle
Goodman	farmer, owner of the house
Greet	cry, weep
Guddling	searching in water, rooting about
Gue	ancient two-stringed fiddle
Gully	large knife
Hairst	harvest, autumn
Half-fletts	long basket made of straw for carrying grain
Hallans	wooden perches for hens
Hogboon	supernatural creature generally living in a mound
Huik	hook, sickle
Ingle	word used instead of fire because of superstitious fears
Kirk	church
Kirn	churn
Kirned	churned
Knockeen-stone	large stone with a big hollow in the top to put corn in. It could then be pounded into meal
Knockit	ground, pounded
Knowe	mound
Kye	cattle, cows
Lavro	lark
Lawrightman	headman of local court, official appointed to uphold laws and regulations
Liora	large, square hole to act as a chimney
Lug	ear
Markal pin	wooden pin to hold on the sock of a plough
Menyie-singers	people who went round the houses to entertain
Messigate	right of way to a church; road taken by those carrying St Magnus's body from Egilsay to Birsay
Mezzies	triangular shaped nets made from straw, used to carry baskets of grain on a clibber saddle
Muckle	large
Neuk	nook, corner
Norn	old language spoken in Orkney, descended from Old Norse
Nousts	trenches dug near a beach for shelter for boats
Oxter	armpit
Oyce	tidal inlet of water from the sea to an expanse of water such as the 'Peerie Sea'
Paese Day	Easter Day
Peerie	small, little. The word used in Orkney now is 'peedie' which has been adopted from Scots as it is similar to the original Norn word 'peerie'. Peedie has been used in Orkney for about 150 years
Pirren	child who walked before the oxen to get them to pull the plough. Probably from 'peerie one'

Quern stone	stone used to grind corn
Red-ware	large-leaved seaweed
Reestid	dried and smoked
Rivlins	shoes of skins strapped to the feet and ankles
Roo	heap, pile
Sallur	other room of house, used as bedroom and storeroom
Selkie	seal
Shalder	oyster catcher
Simmons	straw ropes
Skeklers	people in disguise taking part in festival, e.g. Halloween
Skeo	stone-built shed with gaps between the stones to let air circulate to dry fish or to keep cheese
Skerry	rock covered by the sea at high tide
Ski pin	pin behind the sock on a plough to break up the earth
Skroo	small stack
Skylan board	board at the side of the liora that could be shifted from one side to the other to stop the wind blowing down
Tacksman	someone who collected the rents due on farms
Terran	mythical monster, representing winter
Thaft	seat in a boat
Trow	supernatural creature, mischievous
Tullyie	struggle, fight
Tusker	implement to cut peats, like a spade
Udal Law	old law of Orkney and Shetland, some aspects of which are still in force
Uphelli	festival to welcome back the sun after midwinter
Voar	Spring
Wadmell	kind of rough cloth
Whaap	curlew
Windleens	tied up bundles of straw or hay

SHORT BIBLIOGRAPHY

List of main books used.

Jo Ben: Descriptio Insularum Orchadiarum
Olaf D Cuthbert: A Flame in the Shadows
Alexander Fenton: The Northern Isles
John Firth: Reminiscences of an Orkney Parish
Peter Jamieson: The Viking Isles
Ernest W Marwick: The Folklore of Orkney and Shetland
George Marwick: The Old Roman Plough
Dr Hugh Marwick: The Orkney Norn
James Omond: Orkney 80 Years Ago
J M E Saxby: Shetland Traditional Lore
W P L Thomson: The New History of Orkney
James Wallace: An Account of the Islands of Orkney
Also some pages in the Orkney Archives from an old atlas written in French